Spring
Books London

Birds of Heath and Marshland

BIRDS

of Heath and Marshland

Illustrations by
E. DEMARTINI

Text by
O. ŠTĚPÁNEK

Translated by
A. DENEŠOVÁ

SPRING BOOKS

Designed and produced
by ARTIA for SPRING BOOKS

DRURY HOUSE·RUSSELL STREET·LONDON WC2
© 1962 Artia

First edition 1962
Second impression 1963
Third impression 1964
Fourth impression 1966
Printed in Czechoslovakia

Introduction

We are presenting nature-lovers with another book dedicated to the best-loved members of the animal kingdom—the birds. This is a companion volume to *Birds of Field and Forest*, which was mainly devoted to the small species of birds protected by man for their usefulness to the farmer and orchard keeper in controlling insects and other pests, and for their beauty and delightful song. *Birds of Field and Forest* has been enthusiastically received. Its introductory section, which summed up briefly everything of general interest about birds, included a few words about their anatomy and origin, nesting and migration habits, and their importance to man.

In this volume we have selected for presentation some members of the bird community known as game-birds. For the greater part, these are fairly large birds frequenting our heath and marshland, and of special interest to the sportsman. The term 'game-bird' is not so easy to define as it may appear at first sight. There are as many different opinions as there are countries and nations as to what constitutes a game-bird, and even in any single country views are bound to change on this point over the course of the centuries. The point of view of the inhabitants of Iceland's inhospitable shores and the Faroe Islands is apt to differ from that of the Scottish gamekeeper, and again from the huntsman in the Canadian forests, the Australian bush or on the continent of Africa. Opinions as to which birds are fair game are influenced everywhere by the species indigenous to the country in question, by that country's sporting traditions, its cultural standards, its geographical position and climate, by the economic needs of the population, and similar considerations. The European and American huntsmen of several centuries ago had fundamentally changed their views in this respect compared with those prevailing in ancient times; while today, with so much more known about animal life, they are different again. That is why the term 'game-bird' is not so easily defined, for it includes, for example, both our wild ducks and pheasant. For this volume we have selected mainly such representatives of the birds of heath and marshland as are familiar to the European sportsman and referred to in the game laws of most European states.

There is perhaps no other group of birds with such sharply defined sexual and seasonal differences as the family which comprises most of our game-birds. The appearance of the male often varies from that of the female to such a degree that the layman would not readily identify them as members of the same species. Whereas the males are adorned with brightly-coloured plumage, their mates are drab, their colour merging with the ground on which they sit in their nests. While the males or cock birds will boldly challenge rivals to fight and proclaim their ownership of territory and mates, the females or hens are quiet and demure. Therefore it has been necessary in this book, in order to give some idea of the profusion of shapes and colours prevailing among the larger birds inhabiting heath and marshland, to describe the appearance of the duller females along with the fine dress of their mates. Owing to the limited number of plates that a book of this kind can include, we found it impossible to present the full range of variations; just as it has not been possible to show the difference between summer and winter plumage, nuptial and non-breeding dress, or the chicks in their coats of down, those fluffy little balls in shades of brown, black and grey that we see near the water and woodlands in the summer. Nor could we illustrate the eggs in their manifold shapes and colours, though they are sometimes the best means of identifying the birds residing in our heath and marshland. The birds are a large group, and to include them all this book would have to be a tome. It would not then get into the hands of the wide circle of nature-lovers for whom it is designed. We are not planning an exhaustive and ambitious ornithological study, or a catalogue of species. Its purpose is much simpler: we should like it to be read by young people and sportsmen, and from among their ranks win friends and supporters for the idea of a better protection of birds.

Some General Points

As far back as the dimmest beginnings of life, when our distant forebears were roaming the unfriendly wilderness, it was the birds that first fell victim to human hunger. Birds' eggs, nestlings, clumsy young fledglings, and here and there some adult bird caught unawares, fell prey to the primitive people, just as now they are hunted by the apes. It was the first mode of hunting which did not involve any danger to man, yet yielded many a tasty morsel to the voracious human pack.

8

Women and children, too, were able to contribute in this way to feeding the hungry family, often quite substantially, if they happened upon a nesting bird colony. When a roaming band of men found a place where hundreds of gulls, terns, gannets, ducks or some other colonising birds had made their home, their dietary worries were over for some time, and the hunting of large and dangerous beasts could be postponed or relegated to sport and pastime for the warriors. Even to this day people in remote places eke out their fare in this way, and for them this forms an essential source of food supply. The author saw in the mountains of Crete how the shepherd boys were eagerly searching for the nests of mountain birds, afterwards roasting the nestlings they found over an open fire, to offer to strangers.

From this kind of chance hunting it was only a step to the invention of various hunting implements that would make it possible for man to get a supply of adult birds throughout the seasons in virtually unlimited numbers. In this way, the different tribes thought up the most diversified hunting aids, from slingshots and bows to boomerangs and blowpipes, as well as various snares, traps and nets. Incidental egg collection developed into an intentional, savage and completely uncontrolled bird hunt in various parts of the world. Man hunted birds for their flesh and fat, and later also for their feathers. In places where colonies of birds were nesting, whole communities took part in the hunt, in the same way as seashore tribes concentrate on fishing. The bird hunt accounted for the staple diet, and the flesh of the birds even became a commercial commodity. The puffin was hunted for this purpose, also the gannet, and the great auk in the north, and the penguin in the southern areas.

That is why people in different countries have different concepts of the term game-bird—i.e. those species of bird whose flesh had the best flavour, or whose feathers were best suited to keep people warm in winter. In some cases it applied also to such birds whose feathers were beautiful enough to mark the high-born warrior from the ordinary members of his tribe. In Europe, man hunted the great auk, the gannet, the puffin, the red grouse, the partridge, the quail, the capercaillie, the hazel-grouse, all kinds of mallard and wild geese, swans and herons, as well as almost every sort of small songster. Many species were hunted so thoroughly that they became extinct, such as the northern great auk; others were reduced to very small numbers. For Asia the list of hunted birds was even longer, with the addition of the sand-grouse, the Asian bustards, all species of pheasant, the peacock, the wild Indian grouse and many small birds in the tropical regions. The Aborigines and, later, the white settlers of Australia hunted the black swan, the emu, several species of parrot, the grouse-like guan and large pigeons. On the North American

Continent the chief game-birds were the wild turkey, prairie grouse, the Californian quail, the passenger pigeon and the Canadian wild goose. Millions of passenger pigeons were exterminated by American hunters, never to reappear. In South America hunting went on for the rhea—an ostrich-like runner—the tinamou, and the Brazilian penelope. Humming-birds, toucans and the fierce harpy eagle were killed for their feathers. The African hunted the ostrich, which he decimated in numbers and reduced to living in a corner of its former habitat, also francolin, some species of which he exterminated altogether, Nile geese and tufted ducks, crowned cranes, several species of guinea-fowl and many another birds.

That stage in civilisation was the deadliest to the birds. Man was by now equipped with modern weapons but he had not yet advanced to considering the consequences of his actions and never gave the slightest thought to the preservation of game-birds or their young. In many places the hunt went on until the last bird of a species had been killed. That is what happened to the proverbial dodo—a large flightless bird related to the pigeon, indigenous to Mauritius. In the northern Atlantic seaboard it happened to the great auk, in North America to the passenger pigeon, while in New Zealand it was the moa, etc. A great number of heath and marshland birds suffered the same fate at the hands of the ruthless hunters of the past few centuries, or they were confined to some last refuge where their diminished numbers are still holding out. An example of this was the callous hunt of birds of paradise in New Guinea. At the turn of the century ladies of fashion took such a fancy to the beautiful plumage of the cock that some species of these rare birds are now confined to small areas, where they still live only because of rigorous protection. When a craze broke out in Europe and America for colibri feathers to adorn ladies' hats, the tiny humming-bird, that living jewel of South American wild-life, was hunted and collected in enormous numbers. Before the Second World War, one Paris firm was left with some 250,000 humming-bird skins in its warehouse when fashion decreed that feathers were out!

Neither, if we want to be fair, can we absolve our own Continent from all guilt in this respect. We in Europe sinned almost as much, in respect of the indiscriminate killing of birds, not excepting the smallest of them. Here, too, the hunting of millions of songsters and other small birds went on unchecked for centuries, for the morsels of food they provided. It was primarily in the south European countries, such as Italy, the Balkans and Spain, that year by year whole flocks of house-martins, sand-martins, swallows, warblers, nightingales, larks and other small birds were wiped out on their way south when, tired from their long flight, they rested on those treacherous shores. Nor can we absolve the central European countries of a hundred years ago from all blame. We all know how much fowling used to go on and how many song-birds ended up in the snares and traps of eager hunters. It was not only well-fed fieldfares that fell victim to this sport, but thrushes, blackbirds, redwings, bramblings, chaffinches and larks—in short, every kind of bird that settled in flocks in the crowns of bare trees or flew straight into the nets stretched across their path.

Perhaps the fowling in Europe a century ago serves well to illustrate the change that has occurred during the past fifty years in the attitude of Europeans towards their game-birds. In those days nobody seemed to see anything wrong in the indiscriminate killing of small birds, nor in their being served at table. Fowling was then regarded as an innocent pastime, or even as an irreproachable trade, much as we now look upon fishing or collecting butterflies. Yet nowadays the snaring and catching of birds is abhorrent to most civilised people. Whereas the cookery-books of a century ago gave instructions on the dressing and roasting of lark and swallow, a modern person feels revolted and disgusted at the sight of a dish of plucked song-birds. Every schoolboy now knows that the catching of songsters, especially in migration, is illegal and to be despised as an outrage against nature. In many places protection laws are by now perhaps unnecessary, as people would probably protect their feathered friends from unwonted interference unassisted by the law. We know from experience that such protection is frequently very effective.

And yet, in some parts of Europe, the slaughter and large-scale eating of small birds is taken so much for granted that the law makes not the slightest difference. As recently as 1955, Naples nature-lovers and workers of the Society for the Prevention of Cruelty to Birds confessed to the author with embarrassment that fowling was still widespread in the Italian countryside, and that song-birds were consumed *en masse*. And in 1935, in the households of Greek country folk, the author saw row upon row of neatly stacked jars on top of cupboards, containing carcasses of small birds. The tiny songsters—larks and warblers among the largest—thus ended up cooked in oil, an ornament to the well-run household, just as we preserve pickled onions and gherkins.

Even when the migratory birds have got across the Mediterranean, their troubles are far from over. In Egypt, Tunisia and Algeria, people are eagerly waiting to trap them by the score for the plates of local gourmets. Chief victim is the central European quail, traditionally killed and eaten in their thousands.

With the advance of civilisation man penetrated farther into the mysteries of nature and learned to appreciate birds from the economic and ethical points of

11

view. That is how the first attempts at bird preservation came into being. Laws and regulations were enforced to protect species fast dwindling and on the point of dying out. The indiscriminate killing of birds became unlawful, to be looked down upon in the same way as the poaching of other game. In many places fowling was restricted or altogether forbidden, so that in all civilised countries small birds are now crossed off the list of game-birds. Shooting seasons were restricted, and some species threatened with extinction came to be protected throughout the year. The reckless hunt gradually turned into shooting and game-keeping, and the hunter who killed everything in sight so long as it could be eaten, gave way to the disciplined sportsman. In the place of hunting for booty's sake we now have gamekeeping, i.e. control over reproduction, protection from adverse influences and enemies, as well as planning the future of game-birds. The sportsman himself lays down strict laws for the control of bird shooting; he voluntarily cuts down the open season for certain species, prohibits the hunt outright in certain areas, sets up game reserves, severely punishes poaching, etc. Those species which—after careful scientific study—are declared fair game are helped to increase and provided with food in times of shortage. In short, the gamekeeper does almost as much for game as the breeder does for domestic livestock. All this care is designed to derive the maximum of profit out of controlled shooting, and indeed certain species of game-birds have in consequence become an essential factor in human food consumption, as for example the grouse, partridge and pheasant. Protected species tend to become much more numerous in certain localities so that one might speak of a certain overpopulation of the game-bird stock. This may disturb the biological equilibrium, to be carefully studied by the gamekeeper who tries to restore the proper balance. The natural enemies of the birds are also studied, as are any artificial adverse circumstances influencing the stock, so that scientific gamekeeping has emerged as a new branch of applied zoology.

As a result of scientifically-based gamekeeping the situation has improved with regard to many species of game-birds, and occasionally a certain extension of the natural habitat has been brought about. Yet in the majority of cases help has either arrived too late, or conditions in densely populated countries have made the existence of some species permanently impossible. Their numbers keep dwindling and they frequent an ever diminishing territory. This applies to the central European population of the mountain hazel-grouse, the great and little bustards (the former at one time being common in England, where it could not exist even if reintroduced), and in places to the black grouse and the capercaillie, to some of the ducks, snipe, curlew, etc. All these birds are therefore now protected throughout the year in several countries, or their shooting is at least restricted to a minimum. But it seems desirable and necessary for sportsmen and protectors of game everywhere to avoid shooting certain species of bird permanently, perhaps by crossing them definitely off the game list. Surely it is easy to distinguish between those European birds that come under the heading of economically important table fowl, such as partridge and pheasant, and the category of game-birds which are economically insignificant because of rare or sporadic incidence, as for instance the bustards, snipe, black grouse and hazel-grouse. These latter should be the concern of the gamekeeper only, whose job it would be to preserve them for the interest of future generations. There is a great difference between the care that the semi-domesticated pheasant enjoys at the hands of the gamekeeper and the ordinary protection afforded by the law to many other species in Europe.

Enlightened legislation of this kind would naturally only be effective if carried out on an international scale, as a corollary to the international convention for the protection of birds. What use is it to preserve a certain species of bird in one country only to have it mercilessly killed in another the moment its flocks take off on their journey south? A case in point is the quail which, though protected throughout the season in some countries, is snared and shot at in the south of the Continent either without any restriction whatever or, as is the case in Italy, for too long a period. As the hunt in North Africa is in no way restricted either, the number of quail is still very limited in many parts of its breeding range, in spite of every protective measure. In recent years, international hunting and zoological conferences have concerned themselves with the decrease in the numbers of the mallard, caused perhaps by too intensified shooting or in some cases by the management of fishponds. The preservation of birds is greatly helped by the setting up of reserves in which the game-birds get the peace they need for un-disturbed breeding, and from where they may spread to neighbouring districts where they are scarce owing to past attacks. The reservation, or game-bird re-serve, must of course be sufficiently large and must afford the birds optimum food supplies. For waterfowl and waders large fishpond reserves have proved success-ful, provided that rushes and reeds are not cut down and that fish breeding is conducted so as not to interfere with the bird colony. How attractive such sheltered and still waters are to aquatic and marsh-birds is evidenced by the fact that species will soon move in there, which have not been seen in the vicinity for decades but which may have regarded the place as their normal home at some time in the past.

As mentioned earlier, the concepts of correct and modern gamekeeping ought to envisage the reasonable application of restriction in the shooting of game-birds as a marked decrease in stocks becomes apparent in a given area. The sportsman will then apply strict self-restraint in order to allow the dwindling species to revive and thus prove himself a good manager. Owing to the severe frosts prevailing during the winter seasons of 1941 and 1942, many European countries witnessed a serious drop in their partridge population, in some places by as much as 80 per cent. As this economically important game-bird has only very slowly regained in numbers, a temporary ban on partridge shooting was wisely introduced in some countries, or at least the open season was reduced to a minimum.

The position of our game-birds is greatly aided also by purposeful protection from natural dangers, such as the rigours of winter and natural enemies. The gamekeeper looks after partridges and pheasants in winter by providing light shelters, putting out grain, and in similar ways. Attempts have been made at what is called the cooping-up of partridges in specially prepared shelters where the birds, after being caught for this purpose, spend the winter. They are released again in the spring, fitter and stronger than if they had been exposed to hunger and cold. Another aid is to keep down the number of beasts and birds of prey in the hunting ground, leaving just as many as are needed for maintaining a natural balance, but not letting them increase in numbers to the point where they might jeopardise game-bird stocks. This must not be misunderstood to mean that we should exterminate all predatory creatures: they, too, play their role in preserving healthy proportions in the wild-life of the region. It is predominantly the weak and sickly animals and birds that they destroy, thus acting as agents of natural selection. Wild ducks and geese can also be helped to more favourable living conditions, chiefly by avoiding cutting down in the autumn the rushes and reeds so favoured by fish breeders. Reed-cutting operations by motor-boat with mechanical blades ought particularly to be severely limited to the sectors where no water-fowl are nesting, otherwise we shall never achieve an increase in their numbers. Good results have been obtained with artificial nesting coops and baskets for ducks, concealed in suitable places among the rushes.

The Acclimatisation of Alien Species

Gamekeepers all over the world have tried to enrich the variety of wild-life in their hunting grounds by introducing foreign species of game-birds. This is called acclimatisation. Innumerable experiments of this kind have been carried out on every continent. Results are bound to vary, being influenced both by the choice of species introduced and by the numbers of specimens used. Also, experiments involving species that were quite unsuited to their new surroundings failed dismally, as might have been expected. Nor has there been any marked success in experiments carried out on too small a scale—e.g. with only a few pairs of birds. It would be a mistake to assume that the idea of acclimatising alien game is entirely a modern process, based on scientific and economic considerations. As far back as ancient times, people made attempts to resettle foreign species of animals and birds. We know, for example, that at the courts of Egyptian, Assyrian and Chinese rulers, various kinds of foreign game were left to roam the gardens and parks more or less at will. In the Middle Ages, European kings and princelings had foreign game imported, which they usually released in their game parks or in the forest. In this way the wild rabbit, the fallow-deer and the pheasant arrived on our Continent.

The acclimatisation of the pheasant in western and central Europe is easily the best example of a large-scale and spectacularly successful experiment of this kind. This handsome bird originated in the vast territory stretching from the shores of the Black Sea to the Far East. It is there that a great number of pheasant species developed, frequently with greatly variegated colours in the plumage of the cocks. Geographically, the nearest to us of these was the common pheasant, *Phasianus colchicus*, which was originally a native of the area between the Black Sea and the Caspian. The bird was familiar to the ancient Greeks who conducted campaigns in that region. They appreciated the quality of its flesh and introduced it to the Greek mainland on the Black Sea coast and at other places in the Balkan peninsula. Later, the Romans found the pheasant there and promptly embarked on settling the bird in Italy so that this delicious table-fowl would be freely available at home. The pheasant made its way with the Roman legions to France and Britain, and from there to the rest of the Continent around the 13th century. In the Middle Ages all of west and central Europe recognised the pheasant as an important game-bird. It was kept in pheasantries which are fully described in old chronicles, under the care of specialised game-wardens called pheasant-keepers. It was not until much later that other species of pheasant were brought to Europe, such as the ringed pheasant from Manchuria and China and the green pheasant from Japan. As all these are closely related species, cross-breeding went on in the pheasantries and game parks to such an extent that in some places we can now no longer find the pure *colchicus* that was originally imported so long ago.

Though carried out without the benefit of scientific knowledge, that ancient experiment was an unqualified success. The common pheasant roamed freely in many regions all over Europe, becoming a standard component of wild-life there. It was found to be quite suitable in agricultural parts as it does no appreciable damage to crops, being in fact rather a beneficial bird because its young feed mainly on harmful grubs.

Later attempts at acclimatising other species of pheasant were less successful, whilst several failed completely. One of the latter was the introduction of the larger Reeves' pheasant from China, distinguished by its strikingly long tail feathers. Although this beautiful bird is a native of mountainous country, and there would seem to be no climatic obstacles involved, it failed to gain favour with breeders owing to the excessive roaming instincts of the young cocks. Flocks of them tend to range over the countryside, never returning to their birthplace. They are wont to turn up unexpectedly in any—even the most unsuitable—place, where they fall an easy prey to the huntsman or some predatory creature. Equally unsuccessful were the attempts at resettling the silver pheasant from south China, possibly for climatic reasons. We know, however, that this handsome bird is bred in China and elsewhere in eastern Asia for its decorative qualities, and is also released outdoors. Further acclimatisation attempts with this species might be worth considering. The small golden pheasant and Amherst's pheasant are the most difficult of all to resettle, or so it would seem, because, though repeatedly introduced in European hunting grounds and game parks, they quickly succumbed to birds and beasts of prey, probably due to their brilliant appearance and awkward flight.

Occasionally, experiments at acclimatisation prove unexpectedly successful. It is a well-known fact that the capercaillie is hard to keep healthy for long in confined quarters, or to adapt to changed conditions; and yet the Scandinavian capercaillie was successfully introduced to Scotland as far back as 1837. The experiment at that time was on rather a small scale and the population died out, but it was later reintroduced on a larger scale and is now a permanent feature of Scottish wild-life. The North American wild turkey was released in various places on the European Continent, generally with good results, although wild turkeys have never managed to subsist without some form of assistance. Nevertheless, attempts seemed worth making because of the handsome appearance of the bird and its delicious flesh, which can well hold its own against the domestic variety. The weight of the wild turkey is another point in its favour, as a full-grown cock may attain more than two stone in weight. Released turkeys keep to their home ground well and are usually found in their accustomed places day by day. They spend the night sitting in a tree, safely out of harm's way. The only obstacle to their wider distribution in Europe is the fact that the young turkeys do not stand

16

up well to damp weather, and protracted spring rains always take a heavy toll of the turkey chicks. The same reason prevents any significant increase of the red-legged partridge, a native of south and south-east Europe. During the past hundred years many attempts have been made—some of them on a major scale— to settle this splendid game-bird outside its dry and rocky native haunts. Experiments involving the red-legged partridge, as well as its cousin the Greek partridge, have so far proved unsuccessful. It should be noted here that acclimatisation attempts in Britain have met with greater success and serve as proof that it ought to be possible to settle the red-legged partridge permanently in other places.

Good results have been obtained in the acclimatisation of the decorative Californian quail, which is distinguished mainly by its overhanging crest. This handsome bird has repeatedly been released in European game parks where it flourished and multiplied for many years.

Besides these relatively prosaic acclimatisation experiments there have also been attempts to release more exotic species in European hunting grounds, but without any real hope of their permanent success. Birds used were the Australian emu, the South American rhea, the Brazilian penelope and tinamou.

Acclimatisation experiments are always fascinating, and it is not impossible that other species like the common pheasant will be found of equal adaptability and economic significance. In all experiments of this kind, however, serious thought must be given to the risk of upsetting the natural ecological balance in the biotope by the introduction of alien elements. This is, of course, strictly to be avoided. All creatures living in a given region (biotope) are dependent on their environment as well as mutually interdependent; each of them contributes to the living conditions and helps to create the perfect balance of the biocoenosis. With the introduction of an alien species this balance may be upset both from the economist's point of view and from the point of view of preserving rare species. This generally occurs if the newly introduced species competes vigorously for food with some native species or if it interferes with its nesting habits. What we must realise is that every acclimatisation attempt is to a certain extent a violation of nature's laws and must be well premeditated. Rash experiments, as for example the disastrous introduction of the European sparrow, or such a noxious pest as the starling to Australia and North America, have brought much trouble in their wake.

Enemies and Diseases of Game-Birds

Our game-birds are threatened by a large number of enemies. It is the job of the sportsman and gamekeeper to know and study their natural foes and to keep down their numbers. For the greater part, game-birds are much more exposed to various enemies than other birds. Thanks to man's support they become more numerous in the hunting ground and consequently more conspicuous than other birds. They attract the attention of beasts and birds of prey alike. With a certain overcrowding of the home ground, and owing to their somewhat diminished mobility and relaxed caution, they fall an easy prey to the attacker. In some cases, predatory birds and beasts literally specialise in a certain kind of game-bird, feeding on it almost to the exclusion of all else and hunting it down to the last specimen.

The chief enemies in this connection are the carrion and hooded crows, both of which play havoc with the nests of pheasants and mallards. The hen-pheasant does not bother much about concealing her nest, and as there is often a row of sitting birds side by side in the pheasantries, the clever egg thief has an easy job. It moves systematically from nest to nest, and within minutes scores of hopeful lives are destroyed in the shell. Crows are just as fond of robbing mallards' nests, and when these important game-birds are sitting every crow in the neighbourhood has its beak spattered with yolk, whilst empty shells are found strewn about the lakeside. Ravens, too, although we protect their colonies in some places as natural relics and though we know that they are generally selective in their choice of food, never miss a chance to rob a pheasant's or partridge's nest; the same applies to every member of the corvid clan. Little wonder, then, that the gamekeeper hates the crow and kills it at every opportunity.

Among the predatory birds, it is primarily the peregrine falcon and goshawk that take their toll among adult partridges, weakly pheasants and young ducks, while their less hefty cousin, the sparrow-hawk, finds its booty among the fledglings of these species. When their own nests are filled with hungry nestlings, their need of live prey is particularly great and makes considerable inroads on the birds in the neighbourhood. Even the presence of a single family of falcons, i.e. two adult and four young birds, makes an appreciable effect on game stock. The daily consumption of an adult falcon is about half a pound of flesh, which, reckoned in the average weight of partridge, means up to two birds a day.

Another predatory bird is the rough-legged buzzard, a winter visitor from the north. It is somewhat larger than the common buzzard but its distinctive marks are its feathered legs. It comes south when there is a lot of snow in the north and food is hard to obtain. Then it arrives half-starved and will attack anything afoot if it dares. Again, its booty usually consists of the frail partridges as they crouch in the snow under the hedgerow, but we also find the remains of hen-pheasants and growing pheasants in the entrails of this northern robber. Sometimes, several rough-legged buzzards will invade the countryside together, and then the game-keeper has his work cut out if he wishes to protect his hapless charges from their claws.

Gamekeepers also reproach the common buzzard with attacking game-birds in winter, and anyone who has dissected a buzzard in winter knows that there is good reason behind this charge. But if we consider the benefits conferred by this bird on the agriculturist during the summer when it destroys hosts of rodent pests, such small robberies ought to be forgiven. After all, they occur mainly when the rodents are burrowing beneath the snow and the buzzard gets desperately hungry. It is understandable that it should try the strength of its talons on partridges and other birds of comparable size. The game laws of some countries accordingly protect the buzzard only during the summer, whereas in winter the sportsman has a free hand with it.

When killing birds of prey in the hunting ground it is well to remember that they, too, play an important part in maintaining nature's balance. If these biological laws are tampered with, the composition of the animal community in the area may be adversely affected. A case in point is the story of the peregrine falcon and the saker-falcon in many European countries. These strong, imposing birds chiefly hunt the harmful crow, as well as chasing fast-flying domestic and wild pigeons for sport. In places where the saker-falcon was exterminated and the peregrine falcon severely decimated, the thieving crow now has the upper hand— the powerful enemy that controlled and kept down their numbers is gone, and the crows freely multiply and do their mischief all over the place. Therefore, even such a seemingly clear-cut case as the shooting of birds of prey must be carefully considered, as it represents an interference with the laws of nature. Damage done by other predatory birds, including the larger owls, is not sufficiently serious to be mentioned here. Minor offences ought to be overlooked because most of the large predatory birds and owls are nowadays fairly rare in densely-populated areas and are therefore protected by law almost everywhere.

Game-birds also have many enemies among the mammals. Chief offenders are the members of the marten family, few of which neglect a chance of catching a plump partridge or pheasant. A particularly bloodthirsty beast is the small stoat, which will not spare the life of any unwary partridge it encounters. Its closest relative, the weasel, rather prefers to hunt harmful rodents, so that it compensates for its other crimes.

Game-birds will also suffer when a family of foxes settles near by. The adult fox and vixen will appease their hunger in various ways; they are quite fond of large insects and the softer of the sweet berries, but when they have a brood of whining fox cubs in their lair they will hunt down anything within sight. The fox is strong enough to overcome even the large capercaillie if it catches it unawares. As it causes a great deal of mischief in the crowded pheasantries, the naturalist finds it hard to persuade the gamekeeper to spare the fox. Havoc among the eggs in pheasantries is also caused by the otherwise useful hedgehog, as well as by the lone-hunting badger. Each likes to augment its fare with an occasional yolk or semi-developed embryo. It makes short shrift of the squealing hen-pheasant by rudely chasing it off its nest. That is why gamekeepers like to keep both at a respectful distance from the pheasantries.

Yet a far more dangerous enemy of game-birds than the various bird-eating mammals and birds are the microscopic, invisible enemies of the protozoa family and other internal and external parasites. These frequently kill game-birds in their hundreds, and man is usually unable to do much about it. An example is the malignant coccidiosis caused by parasites of the genus Eimera. Infection spreads largely in places where birds congregate in large numbers, as, for instance, in partridge shelters. The widespread and dangerous threadworm, *Syngamus trachea*, causes a malignant infection of the respiratory system in game-birds, named syngamosis, from the scientific name of the parasite. This feeds on the membranes of the windpipe in partridges, pheasants and pigeons, more rarely in ducks. As is to be expected, the disease spreads just as easily among wild birds as among the domesticated species. The birds have difficulty in breathing, they choke, cough, and in the case of large-scale infection die wholesale. Man's help is not very effective in syngamosis as the smaller song-birds also carry the infection.

Another epidemic that easily spreads to the pheasantries from domestic chickens is foot-rot, a disfiguration of the base of the leg caused by a mite of the genus Cnemidocoptes. Scaly white patches appear on the toes, the birds cannot walk properly, they lose weight and eventually die. Heavy losses on the pheasantries may be brought about by fowl-cholera, a contagious virus disease which spreads to the pheasants from domestic birds. The game-birds die *en masse* within a week of the onset of this disease.

20

PLATES

The Capercaillie

(TETRAO UROGALLUS Linn.)

Largest of European forest birds, the capercaillie may attain a weight of up to 11 lb. (5000 gm.) and a wing-span of 4 ft. 10 in. (1500 mm.). The thick plumage and the broad tail-fan make the adult cock an impressive bird indeed—true big game among our game-birds.

The bird inhabits coniferous woods, more rarely mixed woods, its range extending throughout Europe, from the 68th Parallel to the Bulgarian mountain ranges. After an absence of centuries the capercaillie was reintroduced to the British Isles in 1837, but did not become established until a second colony was imported later. Scandinavian birds were used for the experiment and the capercaillie is now an accepted part of British wild-life, especially in Scotland. To the east, capercaillies were distributed over portions of Asia, as far as northern Mongolia. The species used to be numerous in the forests of Europe, 1200 specimens being shot in Czechoslovakia alone in 1933. Today their numbers are decreasing everywhere, and sensible forest management is required if these fine birds are not to disappear for ever from many countries.

The capercaillie shows well-developed dimorphism, as to weight, size and colouring. Whereas the cock may, in very rare cases, weigh as much as 14 lb. (6000 gm.), the hen is only half its size and hardly ever weighs more than 5 lb. 9 oz. (2500 gm.) The rich, blackish-grey plumage of the cock contrasts with the buff and tan, brightly-banded dress of its mate. The young birds resemble their mother.

Capercaillie cocks are polygamous, and the mating flight is one of the most interesting features of European wild-life, observers counting themselves fortunate if they are able to witness it.

As in the majority of game-birds, the care of the eggs and rearing of the brood is entirely carried out by the hen. Late in April, or early in May, she deposits between six and ten fairly small spotted eggs in the nest, sitting on them patiently for about four weeks. Capercaillie chicks grow fast; their wings are strong enough to allow them to fly out on a low branch to spend the night, as early as ten days after hatching. The nests are exceedingly exposed to danger, which may account for the fast decrease of the capercaillie in densely populated areas.

The Black Grouse

(LYRURUS TETRIX Linn.)

When the snow has disappeared from mountains, heath and birch grove, and the March sun has dried the sheltered places among the undergrowth, that is the time when the male black grouse, or blackcock, a large blue-black bird with lyre-shaped tail feathers can be seen, frequently in large numbers. They strut and hop about the glades, indulge in fighting like domestic cocks, spread out their tail-fans, brush their wings against the ground and utter their sharp mating calls.

Courtship usually begins at early dawn and comes to a climax just after sunrise, when the brown speckled hens, known as greyhens, arrive. The cocks repeat their dancing and fighting again before sunset. The mating season often continues till the month of May.

The black grouse is much smaller than its cousin, the capercaillie, the male adults attaining an average weight of 3 lb. 2 oz. (1500 gm.) only, and the hens rarely weighing more than 2 lb. 1 oz. (1000 gm.). The cock is polygamous and pays no attention whatever to the nest or the rearing of the chicks. Nesting proceeds from May to June. Ten days after hatching, the young birds are able to fly up to a branch and perch there safely for the night. The bird's diet is roughly the same as the capercaillie's, except for the fact that, instead of pine shoots, it usually feeds on the catkins of birch-trees in the spring, in accordance with the different type of region. In summer, black grouse feed on wild strawberries, bilberries, cranberries and raspberries.

The black grouse is widely distributed over Europe and Asia, although in slightly varying forms. The breed of black grouse familiar in Britain differs from the form typical of the Continent, particularly in the colouring of the hen. Different forms have been observed at the eastern end of the bird's range—e.g. in Mongolia, Siberia, etc.

The Red Grouse

(LAGOPUS SCOTICUS Lath.)

The game-bird most typical of British moor and heath is the red grouse, a close relative of the black grouse. It chiefly frequents heather moors and places abounding in berry-growing plants such as the crowberry, on which it feeds. In winter, grouse move down from high grounds to lower levels and are then also encountered in stubble fields where they busily glean their food.

The red grouse is characterised by the russet hue of its plumage and by the fact that it does not change colour in winter, as do several related species. The legs are richly feathered in a shade of grey, in contrast to the uniformly reddish feathers on the rest of the body. Above the eye, particularly the cock's, are fleshy, crescent-shaped protuberances, which are more developed in spring. As in the partridge, variations in colour will often be found in single specimens of grouse, of either a lighter or darker shade.

The red grouse is plentiful in Scotland, Northern England, Ireland and Wales, the inner Hebrides and the Orkneys. The birds have also been introduced to many places—e.g. Norfolk, Suffolk and Surrey, but seldom successfully.

As a nesting ground, the red grouse prefers heather moors and treeless pasture-land from anywhere in the plains up to high in the mountains. The cock usually hovers around, standing guard when the nest is being made. The clutch of between four and seventeen closely speckled eggs is deposited late in April or early in May, though it may be earlier. The cock takes no share in incubating, but will faithfully keep watch over the nest. The chicks are hatched after some three weeks. They grow very quickly, being half-fledged by the twelfth day after birth.

The red grouse has been acclimatised in Belgium and Germany.

The Common Pheasant

(PHASIANUS COLCHICUS Linn.)

That handsome and valuable bird, the pheasant, was probably introduced to western Europe in ancient times, and to central Europe some centuries later. The qualities of the pheasant were recognised by the ancient Greeks who, first meeting it in its Asian homeland of Colchis, took it with them to their own country, whence it found its way to all parts of the then civilised world. This was one of the most successful experiments in the acclimatisation of a foreign species—though lacking any scientific basis—on a scale unrivalled to this day for any free living bird. Today the pheasant forms an intrinsic part of the fauna of many countries, existing without any particular support in many places.

Like the domestic chicken, to which it is quite closely related, the pheasant is a polygamous bird, the beautiful cock being almost totally indifferent to the fate of his family. The eggs, of which there are from eight to twenty in a clutch, are laid during the first half of April and are of a uniformly tan colour. Incubation takes from twenty-two to twenty-seven days. The nest is constructed in a rather haphazard fashion, so that it sometimes happens that the sitting hen's tail feathers protrude on to a path along which people are continually passing. It is nothing short of a miracle that most pheasant nests escape the attention of humans and animals alike. About three weeks after hatching the pheasant chicks try out their wings. Many of them, however, fall an easy prey to predatory beasts and birds, notably to their chief enemy, the crow. Others fail to survive wet weather in May or June, or die of various epidemics.

28

The Ringed Pheasant

(PHASIANUS TORQUATUS Linn.)

The original pheasant, without a white ring around the throat and with reddish-brown plumage on the rump, came from the regions around the Black Sea and the Caspian. Another pheasant, with white-ringed throat and greenish rump, called the ringed pheasant, and indigenous to China, Korea and Mongolia in various allied races, was imported to Europe much later. As all these are closely related species, cross-breeding takes place very readily, so that we can scarcely find the original, pure race in Europe today. It is claimed that the eastern ringed pheasant brought an increase in the weight of the cocks to the old European pheasantries, but also a greater predilection for roaming.

The Japanese Pheasant

(PHASIANUS VERSICOLOR Linn.)

The plumage of the beautiful Japanese pheasant possesses uncommon vividness as well as an attractive green gloss. Though usually classified as a distinct species *(Phasianus versicolor)*, it does not seem to deviate from membership of the common pheasant race as it can be successfully cross-bred with all the other pheasant races, producing hybrids of outstanding loveliness.

The diet of young pheasants—as in the majority of game-birds—consists of animal matter almost to the exclusion of all else, ninety per cent of it being formed by insects. Very often the latter are the kind of agricultural pest that appear in hosts, so that the pheasant must be considered to be a very useful bird indeed. True, in maturity the percentage of insect food drops sharply, being replaced by vegetable matter, but even at that stage the pheasant cannot be called an agricultural parasite as it subsists largely on the seeds of field weeds.

The Common Partridge

(PERDIX PERDIX Linn.)

In early spring, the fluting call of the common partridge can be heard in the fields. Late February and early March is the courtship season, when the cocks search out their quiet mates and carry on duels with their rivals. The courtship, which lasts till the end of April or even longer, is an ardent one. When the nest is made, the hens lay the first of the uniformly olive-drab or grey eggs. Though the cocks do not attend to the immediate business of nest-building, they do show concern for the safety of their future family by keeping a sharp look-out in the vicinity. Partridges strike up partnerships which last for the period of breeding and rearing their progeny, perhaps even longer. Both parents guard the fledglings jealously from any foe of minor strength, while in the presence of a superior enemy they will employ the well-known ruse of pretending to be wounded, fluttering about the attacker in order to distract his attention from the chicks. If the mother bird is killed, the cock will rear his offspring himself.

The hen usually lays between ten and fifteen eggs, though clutches of up to twenty-four are not unknown. If the partridge pair happens to lose the eggs through some misfortune during incubation the female may lay another lot, which, however, will be fewer in number. Twenty-three to twenty-five days later the lively little chicks hatch out. They are not well equipped to withstand wet weather, and their successful rearing depends on a fine and dry early June. In a rainy season the chicks may perish wholesale. A severe winter may aggravate matters. During the bitter winter and wet spring of 1940–41 about eighty per cent of the partridge population of central Europe perished.

The partridge is a typical native of heath and open fields, its distribution being dependent on grain-growing. The birds' fare is seventy per cent vegetable matter, supplemented in the nesting period by various insect pests. As the vegetable diet is predominantly composed of weeds, the partridge is a useful bird to the agriculturist, quite apart from the excellent quality of its flesh and its prevalence, two factors which make the birds an important budget item in some areas. In consequence, game experts in many countries are doing their best to see that stocks of partridge regain their former strength.

The Quail

(COTURNIX COTURNIX Linn.)

The choice of nesting grounds of the partridge is shared by its lesser relative, the quail. Its favourite haunts are fields of clover and lucerne, fallow land, dry meadows and, less frequently, cornfields. In addition to fair amounts of vegetable matter, the quail—like the partridge—consumes various insects, grubs, larvae and worms. Insects are the staple diet of the young birds.

The pairing season lasts from the end of April till July. During that time the cocks keep up their musical call day and night, engage in fighting and in pursuit of the hens. In contrast to the habits of the partridge, however, their mated life bears no traces of fidelity or gentleness. The quail cock is a bullying, domineering bird, knowing neither faithfulness to its mate, nor affection for its young. In June the hen incubates six to twelve, in rare cases even eighteen, speckled eggs, and three weeks later the small, banded chicks are hatched. The hen leads them about until they learn to take care of themselves. By the nineteenth day they are fully fledged.

The quail is the only game-bird subject to the migratory instinct, undertaking two lengthy journeys each year, in September or October, from its breeding grounds in Europe to the south, and back again in April or early May. These trips take most quails as far as North Africa. Their migration also spells their doom, as they perish in large numbers in the beams of lighthouses, in the sea, or in the nets of the busy fowlers around the Mediterranean. The birds are caught and eaten by the million, year in, year out. In 1936 more than 300,000 live birds were sent to England alone from Egypt, where quails congregate from all over Europe and consequently are caught wholesale.

The senseless killing that used to go on in every country through which the birds passed so decimated their numbers in Europe that in some areas they are now rare birds.

36

The Woodcock

(SCOLOPAX RUSTICOLA Linn.)

Since the beginning of time, snipe and woodcock have been particularly attractive to sportsmen. This great interest is to some extent due to their secretive habits, their life being more or less nocturnal, and not yet investigated in every detail. Lying in wait on a quiet spring evening for the snipe's mating flight to begin has a special, unforgettable fascination. Nor is the snipe to be despised as a table bird, prepared according to traditional recipes.

Largest of this group is the woodcock, of roughly the same size as the turtle-dove, and attaining a weight of 11–15 oz. (300–380 gm.). The slender beak is extremely long, sometimes measuring $1\frac{1}{2}$ in. (36–39 mm.) or more. No less striking are the bird's large black beady eyes, set far back in the sides of the head. The sexes are alike in general appearance; there is no sexual dimorphism, as in the true game-birds and the duck family. Some authorities claim that the females grow somewhat larger.

The woodcock ranges over a vast territory, from Britain to Japan, from the chilly north of the 62nd—64th Parallel to the south of Europe—e.g. Bulgaria. In milder regions the woodcock remains the whole year round, while individuals breeding farther to the north migrate to warmer parts. The ringing of woodcock throws some light on its movements in winter. Woodcocks ringed as nestlings in central Europe were found in Britain the next winter, while others spent the winter in France and Corsica. Woodcocks generally return very early from their winter quarters, sometimes as early as the last third of March. This return in the spring is carried out with a great deal of noise and often stormy courtship, while in the autumn the birds disappear quietly, at night, usually one by one.

The woodcock does not mate for life, and after the breeding season both males and females return to a solitary life. The female builds the nest, hatches out the eggs and rears her brood without assistance. During the latter half of April we find four spotted eggs in the nest, and after three weeks' incubation the pretty chicks can be seen near by, in their mottled, russet down. They cannot be easily identified as woodcock chicks because, in contrast to the hen, their beaks are quite short.

The Common Snipe

(CAPELLA GALINAGO Linn.)

Best known of the marshland-snipe is the common snipe, which compares in size with the thrush and generally weighs no more than 3–4 oz. (100 gm.). It is a thickset bird with a strikingly long beak—$2^1/_2$–3 in. (64–74 mm.) and large beady eyes. The sexes are alike but, as a rule, the female is somewhat larger than the male.

The common snipe avoids undergrowth and is never found in forests. Its favourite habitats are wide marshy meadows, muddy low banks of ponds and wet ground around lakes. When searching for food, the snipe moves in a way reminiscent of the greenshank. When disturbed it will take off in rapid zigzag flight, coming to rest again in the near-by high grass. It usually rests during the day and is liveliest towards dusk or at night.

From the middle of February, birds start moving to their intended breeding ground. When they arrive mating is soon in full swing, the males executing acrobatic turns in the air. The harsh, bleating cry accompanying the nuptial flight has earned the snipe many names derived from the goat or from goat-like sounds. Bleating notes are also employed as warning calls.

The males leave their mates immediately after pairing. The female finds a suitable depression in the ground which she lines with ordinary grass, in which are deposited four pear-shaped yellowish or greenish spotted eggs. This happens in April or early May. The downy chicks emerge after about twenty days.

The common snipe is a northern bird, ranging over a wide territory from Iceland and Great Britain in the west, to eastern Turkestan and Kamchatka in the east, as well as in North America. It is rarer in the south of Europe, being familiar in France, around the Pyrenees, in Italy and in the Balkan Peninsula. It spends the winter wherever the marshlands do not freeze over—i.e. where sufficient food is available, for example in the southwest of England and in Italy. The majority of the northern kind, however, fly south for their winter quarters, many as far as North Africa. They usually take off in September, sometimes in late August, frequently congregating in large flocks for migration.

Although the common snipe is shot, like the woodcock, it is of little economic importance, owing to its sporadic occurrence and small size, even though it is an excellent table bird.

The Great Snipe

(CAPELLA MEDIA Lath.)

The great snipe, which is somewhat larger than the common snipe, breeds in the north of Europe and Asia. From August till October the birds prepare for migration, moving to their winter quarters in central Europe, and to the west, where the marshes do not freeze over. They spend the winter months in Britain, France and Germany, also in Czechoslovakia, Hungary and elsewhere on the Continent, particularly in mild weather.

The great snipe is a native of Scandinavia and the entire north of the Soviet Union. There, it sometimes breeds even farther south, even extending to the Caucasus and Poltava. In northern Germany the great snipe nests only in a very few places but has frequently been observed there during the breeding season.

According to several observers the great snipe prefers drier places in swampland, in contrast to the other species of snipe, and its favourite haunts are meadows where the grass grows tall. In the tundra it likes to keep to low undergrowth on mossy ground. During the mating season it will defend its territory against any member of its species.

When disturbed during the day, the great snipe is reluctant to rise and will rather try to run away from the attacker. When forced to take to the wing, it quickly drops to the ground again after a short, quick flight, usually with plaintive cries. It is, however, a good flier and said to migrate as far as the southern tip of Africa and Asia in winter.

According to Siberian observers the great snipe there executes its mating dance on the ground, so that local sportsmen miss the particularly exhilarating experience of observing the wooing cock in flight. In this mating dance the cocks bristle their wing feathers, excitedly run around the hens and call in a quiet, almost whispering voice. These dances continue until the female begins to sit on the eggs. Nesting takes place a little later, usually at the end of May or the beginning of June. There are four eggs, although of much lighter colour than those of the common snipe.

The Jack Snipe

(LYMNOCRYPTES MINIMUS Bruun)

Smallest of the European snipe, hardly bigger than the skylark, is the northern jack snipe. Its little beak measures $1^1/_2$ in. (39–44 mm.) and its legs are not usually longer than 1 in. (24 mm.). It is an altogether charming miniature of the common snipe.

The jack snipe is only a winter or autumn visitor in west and central Europe, arriving when the frost drives it from its northern home. Then it flies to places where the ground does not freeze, stopping on its way in Britain, France and West Germany, and ending its journey in Italy or Greece. This is where most of the birds spend the winter, others crossing the sea to the north of Africa. The Asian variety goes south to India. For its winter quarters the jack snipe likes to choose flooded fields where it associates in flocks of thousands of birds. In early March the homeward flight begins.

The jack snipe nests in Scandinavia, in many places along the northern coast of Germany, and in the northern portion of the Soviet Union, particularly in Siberia.

The Common Curlew

(NUMENIUS ARQUATA Linn.)

Largest of the snipe-like marsh-birds is the common curlew, which compares in size with the teal and weighs about 1 lb. 8 oz. (700 gm.). It has long legs, upward of $3^1/_4$ in. (80 mm.), so that among its smaller relatives it seems to be strutting about on stilts. Its beak, which is slightly bent, measures up to almost 7 in. (160 mm.).

This species is resident in northern European countries, although it is also known to nest in more southerly places. It is as much at home in the British Isles as in the Soviet Union, where it is to be found as far south as the 48th Parallel, for instance east of the Volga. To the north, it is a native of Scandinavia, Finland, North Germany and the entire north of the Soviet Union. In central Europe the curlew breeds in eastern Czechoslovakia and in Poland. In autumn curlews congregate in large flocks; bird-watchers have reported flocks of several thousand birds. Migration sometimes starts as early as late August, while the birds return from their winter quarters in March or April. Even outside this period individual smallish flocks range over the Continent, and the curlew can be seen outside its regular breeding grounds throughout the year. As a rule, the common curlew spends the winter in North Africa, or still farther south, but some birds stay on in southern Europe in a mild winter, or in Switzerland and the British Isles. In this case, however, it is hard to imagine what the large marsh-bird finds to subsist on. It seems that, in addition to various grubs and larvae, crustaceans, worms and small fish, it supplements its fare with plant food.

The common curlew's nest is a shallow depression in the ground, lined in a slapdash fashion. In April or May the female lays four pear-shaped eggs which are sharply pointed at one end, their ground colour being olive-green marked with spots, and the size similar to ducks' eggs. In contrast to the true snipe, both parents care for their offspring. The baby curlews are charming little creatures with comparatively short beaks but long, wobbly legs.

A chance experiment carried out in Belgium proved that the curlew reaches a very great age. A specimen there lived in captivity for thirty years.

The Lapwing

(VANELLUS VANELLUS Linn.)

An ornament to heath and marshland is the handsome and elegant lapwing. It is a member of the plover family which is closely allied to the snipe, although in appearance it does not much resemble the latter. Its decorative crest and gleaming feathers make the lapwing appear almost exotic among the more sober European bird community. Incidentally, the lapwing has a number of relatives in the tropics.

Lapwings are clever and courageous birds, which will fearlessly attack anyone approaching their nests, even if much larger in size. Uttering their harsh, wailing cries, lapwings may attack grazing cattle, while a flock of the birds may even dare to measure their strength against predatory beasts. The lapwing quickly sums up man's intentions, and when it sees a sportsman with his shining gun will keep flying in front of him, at a safe distance, constantly warning other birds in the neighbourhood by its behaviour and cries. It is a great achievement to get within shooting distance of the lapwing or to shoot other birds while a lapwing is on guard near by.

In a mild winter, lapwings return to their intended nesting places as early as the middle of February. At that time of year they frequent the fields in flocks, being particularly fond of running behind the ploughman to peck some titbit from the soil. But the main return from winter quarters takes place in the middle of March, when the birds move to their breeding places and commence their ardent courtship. By the end of March we find the first eggs already in the nests. The nest is a simple depression in the ground among grass and marshy growth. The relatively large eggs are olive-drab in colour, with black spots, resembling the eggs of the black-headed gull. In some countries lapwings' eggs are collected and sold as delicacies.

The European lapwing is distributed over a vast territory, being as much at home in north, west and central Europe as in Morocco and Turkestan. Nesting places vary, for ringing has established that a bird may nest in England, the next time in Czechoslovakia, and for the third time in West Germany or thousands of miles away, in the Soviet Union. Ringing has also furnished information on the lapwing's life-span which appears to be some ten years.

In winter the lapwing travels either to hot countries (Africa, India, South China), or makes do with more local fare in England or in southern Europe.

The Golden Plover

(CHARADRIUS APRICARIUS Linn.)

A native of north temperate and subarctic regions in the extreme north up to the coast of the Bering Sea, is the elegant, colourful golden plover, a distant relative of snipe and lapwing. It breeds in large numbers on tundra and heath in Iceland and Scandinavia, the British Isles and North Germany, its range stretching east as far as the Siberian Yenisey river. It is less common in central and southern Europe, its most southerly nesting grounds being in Germany and in the Soviet Union, as far south as Leningrad, and in Lithuania.

All over this huge territory the golden plover is widely distributed. Four more or less mottled, olive-buff eggs are deposited in the shallow nest. The males execute intricate aerial acrobatics above the sitting females, often to the accompaniment of loud, melodious whistling. Care of the nest and of the brood is the concern of both parents, carried out with great alertness and devotion. The young birds are precocious, leaving the nest soon after hatching and being able to conceal themselves skilfully from their enemies, like the nestlings of the lapwing. This skill stands them in good stead, as these gentle birds have numerous foes.

In winter the golden plovers set out on the long trip south, putting in appearances on the way in places where they are unknown in the summer. They will then feed around the water edge, as well as in stubble fields where they fall victim to sportsmen after other game. The flesh of the plover—as of all related birds—is highly valued table-fare, therefore the birds are caught in nets in some localities. They are, however, fairly small in size, attaining a weight of scarcely 7 oz. (190 gm.). The golden plover generally spends the winter around the Mediterranean shores, although some of the birds have been seen farther to the north, in central Europe. They return to their breeding grounds towards the end of March or later, being then of far less striking appearance than in the autumn.

The Coot

(FULICA ATRA Linn.)

The coot is a true aquatic bird, rarely leaving its native element. This may be because it is a clumsy and awkward walker. Though a fair flier, it can hardly be induced to take to the wing. When forced to do so it will usually only cross to the other end of the lake, running across the surface of the water rather than flying, using its short wings only to help it along. That is why during duck-shoots several hundred coots are sometimes bagged on a single lake.

Strangely enough, however, the coot manages to go on long winter migrations, as the ringing of the birds and the international co-operation of bird-watchers have testified. The majority spend the winter around the Mediterranean, either on the European or the African side. The birds have been met in Spain, Italy and Greece, also on the Nile, in the Canary Islands, India, Celebes, Java, and even in Australia. It is common in Britain. The coot sometimes makes its winter quarters on non-freezing lakes in Switzerland.

Before taking off for their winter homes the birds gather in large numbers on lakes or rivers, generally not before November. They return north in early March to be home for the breeding season. Coots breed virtually everywhere in the Old World, approximately from the 57th Parallel down to north-western Africa, Egypt, India, Japan and South Siberia.

After arrival in the breeding grounds the males with their large, startlingly white, bald foreheads, begin to court the similarly-adorned smaller females, and soon we find the first eggs in the large pile-shaped nests. They are light tan in colour with small spots. After about three weeks of incubation between five and nine black baby birds with orange heads and beaks emerge, swimming around the nest with great agility immediately after hatching. Growing very slowly, the young birds generally learn to use their wings when they are two months old.

Sexual dimorphism is not very pronounced in the coot, the main difference between the sexes consisting in their weight. The male adult generally weighs 2 lb. 2 oz. (1000 gm.), whereas the female hardly ever exceeds 1 lb. 3 oz. (600 gm.). The wing-span of the males is also greater.

Coot's flesh is not usually regarded as a delicacy; the fat it puts on abundantly at the close of the summer is almost useless owing to its unpleasant smell. Nevertheless, the birds are shot in large numbers, and in southern Europe even caught in nets.

The Moorhen

(GALLINULA CHLOROPUS Linn.)

Where the ponds are thick with water-plants, their surface almost covered with the floating pads of various kinds of water-lilies, the slender moorhen makes its home. A close relative of the water-rail, it deftly moves across the surface of the pond, giving a curious effect of running along the water; yet closer observation shows that the bird's exceedingly long toes find sufficient support on the stems of half-submerged plants and on lily-leaves floating on the water.

The moorhen is distributed all over Europe, including Britain. Its range extends from latitude 64° north in Sweden down to North Africa, from the British Isles to Turkestan. It migrates to the Mediterranean from colder regions and stays on throughout the year in milder countries where the waters do not freeze over completely. Migrating moorhens return to their nesting grounds around April.

The nest is made from broken bits of reeds and carex and placed in a reed thicket, frequently in the shape of a floating platform. During the second half of May the female deposits between six and eight yellowish, slightly mottled eggs. The chicks, as in all the rails, are agile and independent from birth.

The moorhen subsists on a mixed diet of animal and vegetable origin. A charming member of our marsh-bird tribe, it deserves our full protection.

The Water-Rail

(RALLUS AQUATICUS Linn.)

A somewhat mysterious bird is the slight water-rail, an inhabitant of damp, thickly overgrown places, which is rather more often heard than seen. Hiding among the reed beds on the banks of slow-moving rivers, in marshland and bullrush thickets by neglected lakes, or in swamps with tall water-plants and near boggy pools, its loud call rings out on calm nights. The water-rail's voice is loud enough to suggest a far larger bird, and it is hard to believe that the small creature we may at times glimpse is responsible for this great noise among the rushes.

Its elongated beak sets the water-rail apart from the other members of its family. In size it corresponds roughly to the common snipe, its weight not exceeding 4 oz. (115 gm.) but attaining a wing-span of some 16 in. (415 mm.).

The water-rail inhabits almost all of Europe, from north to south, from east to west, being at home even on the chilly moors of Iceland. It is also a native of North Africa and western Asia. It is a point of interest that the birds are frequently found on very remote isles though they are poor fliers.

Its reluctance to take to the wing caused old text-books to claim that the water-rail migrates on foot. The flight is slow and clumsy, so that the birds often collide with power and telegraph lines. Moreover, they usually migrate by night.

Return to the breeding grounds takes place in mid-April, but may be earlier or later. The water-rail remains throughout the winter in some places, but if it does it roams chiefly along the waterways in search of food. The nest is made from broken bits of water-plants and situated in a well-concealed place. The clutch comprises between six and twelve creamy white eggs with dark spots, incubated by both parents alternately. Nineteen to twenty-one days later the chicks emerge, fluffy and agile.

The water-rail's diet is mixed, consisting of small creatures, from beetles to frogs and small fish, supplemented by various berries and the shoots of water-plants.

The Great Bustard

(OTIS TARDA Linn.)

At one time common in Britain, especially in the region of Salisbury Plain, but now a typical inhabitant of open steppe-like country, is the largest of European birds, the great bustard. Its build and field character are ideally suited to the wide, endless plains where the short steppe grass grows, or where acres of maize, corn and vegetable crops are planted. The full-grown cock stands more than three feet tall and has amazingly acute eyesight, this combination allowing it to command so wide a view that it is difficult for any foe to approach unnoticed. The long, strong legs with their three short, thick toes reveal the accomplished runner, able to hold its own against the ostrich. Also, the bustard is a relatively good flier, and is capable of covering considerable distances in a straight line on its short but broad wings. Its colouring perfectly merges with the dusty grassland that it haunts; it is a bird uncommonly well adapted to its habitat. Yet it has one bad foe, which often helps to bring about its undoing, namely thick fog, under the cover of which an approaching enemy may close in. Bustard hunters, taking advantage of the fact that the birds are not shy of grazing livestock, will often kill them by taking cover behind a horse or farm vehicle.

In past times the great bustard used to be a far more frequent inhabitant of the wide open spaces of Europe, but the birds are nowadays only to be found in southern Czechoslovakia, Hungary, the Balkans, and on the steppes of the Soviet Union. They are also at home in Asia Minor and North Africa. Single birds will sometimes straggle west to Germany, or even England. For the most part these are immature birds, perhaps travelling to places where the great bustard's forebears used to breed.

The great bustard is really a huge bird, with a weight of 32 lb. (16 000 gm.) not unusual for a full-grown cock. The much smaller hen may attain a weight of up to 13 lb. (6000 gm.). The male has a wing-span of some 8 ft. (2400 mm.), the female of about 6 ft. (1700 to 1800 mm.)

Great bustards breed in early May, the clutch of eggs comprising only two, more rarely three. Eggs and chicks are looked after solely by the hen, who cares for her family until the autumn.

The Little Bustard

(OTIS TETRAX Linn.)

A lesser relative of the great bustard is the little bustard, a bird about the size of the domestic chicken, whose appearance and mode of life, however, closely resembles that of the larger species. The plumage is more colourful, particularly in the cock, but the feet and wings are similar. The little bustard, too, loves wide open spaces, avoiding clumps of tree or bush-land. It only relaxes this rule when it comes upon vineyards, in which it is exceedingly fond of grazing. Otherwise, it favours grassy steppelands and untilled fields, also maize, clover and cornfields. In autumn it may make do with an overgrown potato patch for want of anything better. The little bustard gives a wide berth to agricultural land at all times, being extremely wary of human company, but there is not much choice left to it in present-day Europe. Though it has adapted itself somewhat to changed conditions, it is a much rarer bird today than it was a hundred years ago. With advancing land cultivation there has been a drastic reduction in the little bustard population, which will surely disappear from Europe altogether, as it has done from Britain, unless the strictest protection is introduced and sufficiently large reserves established.

This bird nests regularly—but in small numbers—in southern Hungary, Bulgaria, Yugoslavia, the south-eastern parts of the Soviet Union, in Asia Minor, Iran, India and in North Africa. Only exceptionally will it breed in western Europe—e. g. in Spain, France, Italy, the western regions of Germany, and in Sardinia. It occurs from time to time in Britain. Its numbers, however, are rapidly diminishing everywhere.

The little bustard's choice of food does not differ from that of its larger relative, nor is there any great difference in its family life. The mating season occurs in the latter half of May, after which three or four brownish or greenish mottled eggs appear in the simply-made nest.

60

The Little Grebe

(PODICEPS RUFICOLLIS Pallas)

Our waters are the home of yet another group of birds which belongs to the duck, goose and lapwing community enlivening our ponds and lakes. This is a small family of diver birds in which the three front toes are united by a fold of skin instead of being webbed. They are truly water-fowl, awkward and clumsy on dry land and therefore loath to leave the water. They even build their nests so that their young, the moment they are hatched, can slip straight into the water.

The smallest is the little grebe, which scarcely attains the size of the quail and usually weighs no more than 9 oz. (250 gm.). The comparatively short wings and very short steering feathers make the body of the little grebe look almost like a ball.

Its range extends all over the temperate zones of Europe, Asia and Africa, while it is also to be found in the Indo-Australian region. Rarer in the north, the little grebe is among the less numerous birds in the south of Sweden and the British Isles. It abounds all over central Europe, and is to be found among the birds nesting on some lakes on the Nile.

The little grebe makes do with the smallest pool as a nesting place so long as it is thickly covered with water-plants around the margins. The bird dives for food as well as for safety and can stay under water for an incredibly long time. If we watch closely, we can see how the little grebe—concealed somewhere under the large pad of a water-lily or behind a blade of rush—cautiously raises its beak above the surface for breathing. It will not surface as long as it sees some danger lurking on the bank. Even the youngest of the little grebe's brood are adept at this trick, and they are almost impossible to catch even though they are less than a few feet away.

In May the little grebe makes its nest, which is situated directly on the water and has the appearance of a pile of mud and rotting sticks of reed. The bird collects the material for it from the bed of the pond during its diving forages. In May or June four or six bluish eggs are deposited in the nest, later changing colour to a dirty brown.

The Great Crested Grebe

(PODICEPS CRISTATUS Linn.)

Largest representative of the grebes in Britain and Europe is the great crested grebe, easily identified by its distinctive wide feather ruff and rosette-shaped crests. When excited, it spreads and unites these ornaments to form a queer and imposing head-dress.

The great crested grebe is no rarity on our waters, yet we never see many of the birds together. There are usually only one or two pairs nesting on even a large-sized lake. The birds are exceedingly wary as in some places they are much harassed by fishermen. The great crested grebe is something of a glutton, consuming up to $10^1/_2$ oz. (300 gm.) of small fish—of a length of up to 8 in. (200 mm.)—daily. So it is not to be wondered at that fish breeders cannot tolerate the birds on a pond where young industrial fish have just been introduced. However, on a large lake with full-grown fish the birds' appetite does not really make any difference. In such places the great crested grebe is in fact a useful bird as it keeps down the number of coarse fish.

The great crested grebe usually arrives at its favourite waters in the latter half of March, taking off again in September or October. Though short of wing and rarely aloft in the summer, the birds cover amazing distances during migration, and ringing has shown that great crested grebes arrive almost a thousand miles from home in a very short time.

The nest is made of crushed bits of reeds and rushes and is built directly on the water, looking like a small floating islet among the reeds. During the second half of May the nest contains between three and six bluish (later turning to reddish-brown) eggs of about $2^1/_4 \times 1^1/_2$ in. (55 $\times$ 37 mm.). The young birds are excellent swimmers and divers and can be seen resting on their mother's back on the water.

The Common Heron

(ARDEA CINEREA Linn.)

Overgrown waterways rich in fish, where willow and poplar trees form impenetrable thickets, and where sandy shallows alternate with stretches of fine mud—that is where the common heron makes its home. We also find this splendid member of the European bird community in fens and marshy groves where the water lingers long under the tall trees in spring, and by tree-bordered lakesides. There it stands, motionless in the water's current on its long slender legs, watching patiently for the small fish that are its staple diet. Nor is the heron a modest eater: from observation based on the eating habits of captive birds we know that the daily consumption of the 3 lb. (1300 gm.) heron is approximately $5\frac{1}{2}$ oz. (150 gm.) of fish. No wonder the birds are unpopular with fishermen, even though they also catch frogs, water-rats and shrews, as well as an occasional mole on the bank. In some places herons are therefore killed on sight, and consequently the birds have become rarer in some parts of Europe than they used to be.

Herons live in virtually every country of the Old World, with the exception of cold areas. Their range does not extend beyond about 58° north in Siberia. From August onwards heron families begin to migrate, taking off in earnest on their long trip south in September, passing through countries where they do not normally breed. They fly as far south as North Africa; and ringing has helped to establish that European herons get as far as the Canaries.

The birds usually nest in colonies in tall trees, often in large numbers. More than a hundred nests have been counted over a small area. The heron is easily recognised in flight by the posture of its neck, which is quite different from that of the stork, although both birds are of roughly the same size. Whereas the stork stretches out its neck in flight, the heron draws its neck into an S-shaped curve. The wing-span of the heron measures from 5 ft. 2 in. (1560 mm.) to 6 ft. (1830 mm.).

The Bittern

(BOTAURUS STELLARIS Linn.)

Anybody on a night errand, walking by reed-grown margins of lakes, might be startled by a loud, booming voice coming from the darkest spot among the bullrushes. If the wanderer is brave enough to venture into the reed jungle to find the owner of the voice, he is likely to return without having achieved his object, for there is little trace of the mysterious nocturnal creature. Little wonder, then, that the people of long ago made up fairy-tales about the shadowy marshlands, ascribing supernatural powers to the ghost which they believed they heard calling in the night.

The nocturnal creature that frightened them was meanwhile standing, shadow-like, at the edge of the water, more like a tree stump than a bird, among clumps of reed. From time to time the small shadow would bend over the water, and at once that loud, mournful call would issue forth into the silence of the night. If anyone came closer to investigate the little figure would dissolve, as if by magic, into the darkest shadows among the tall reed stalks.

The 'ghost' is nothing more than a medium-sized bird of the heron family—the bittern. Its thick, soft feathers are coloured to give the body the appearance of a tree stump, an illusion further heightened by the crouching posture and stealthy movements of the bird.

The bittern attains roughly the size of the domestic cock, with a wing-span of some 4 ft. 3 in. (1300 mm.). Despite its comparatively small body the bird appears to be larger, due to its big head and extraordinarily thick feathers. Its head is generally pulled in and the neck drawn into an S-curve. The bittern is inclined to get out of danger's way on foot to avoid leaving the cover of the reeds. Its nest is also skilfully concealed among the reeds. The clutch of four to seven olive-grey eggs is sometimes deposited as early as April.

Though among the most typical of reed birds, bitterns are comparatively rare. It is likely that they lose many of their nests—and their offspring—in reed-cutting operations. Another reason may be the fact that many an adult bird, too, falls victim to the gun during the duck-shooting season.

The bittern spends the winter among the non-freezing lakes in the south of Europe.

The Goosander

(MERGUS MERGANSER Linn.)

Ornithology books once placed the goosander in a special family separate from the other ducks, mainly because of its unusual beak, which is long and narrow, with long saw-like serrations on the edges, quite unlike the flattened bills of other ducks. In contrast with other birds of the duck tribe the goosander's diet consists largely of fish, and its odd beak is also better adapted for this purpose.

Goosanders are exclusively water-fowl, and rarely venture on to dry land. They are excellent swimmers and divers and can stay under the surface for up to two minutes, catching and consuming fish up to 6 in. in length.

The bird is a native of the coasts of Scotland, Scandinavia, Iceland, Denmark and Germany, also of Finland, the Soviet Union and the North American continent. Colonies of goosanders have been known to settle by some inland lakes—e.g. in Switzerland. Their colonies can also be found along large rivers in the summer. The birds' habitat extends as far north as the Polar Circle.

Goosanders begin their migration in October. They can then be seen along the coast of the Continent, but also farther inland, as they move south along the waterways. The birds have been observed inland as late as May, or even later.

The goosander makes its nest in some hollow, either in a tree or in a rock. On the coastline, where the birds are at home, people hang up large nesting boxes in the trees, and the birds promptly move in. However, this is no act of charity but a ruse to collect more easily the large, pleasant-tasting eggs, which are buff or grey in colour and measure up to $2^1/_2 \times 2$ in. (60×50 mm.). The nests are lined with whitish down, which is also put to good use by the collectors. The goosander's plumage is very thick and soft, so that in some localities the birds are skinned and high quality furs are made from their skins. The flesh of the goosander is poor eating, according to our tastes, as is usually the case when birds subsist on fish. But people of the northern shores value the goosander as a table-fowl.

In size the birds correspond to the mallard, reaching a wing-span of up to 3 ft. 8 in. (1110 mm.). The goosander is a wary bird, and difficult to approach. It is quite gregarious, but only within its own species, gathering in large flocks in winter and during the breeding season.

The Smew

(MERGUS ALBELLUS Linn.)

A beautiful bird indeed, the smew, which can be seen on various inland waters in the winter, is the smaller cousin of the species overleaf. It is a plump bird, with a wing-span not exceeding 2 ft. 5 in. (750 mm.). Its weight varies from 1 lb. to 1 lb. 9 oz. (500–790 gm.).

The drake is distinguished by its rich white plumage, which is almost unrivalled within the duck tribe. On the bleak winter waters this snow-white bird easily attracts attention, rather to its misfortune, in places where it is unprotected. Shooting these lovely northern birds is unnecessary as their flesh smells too strongly of fish to be attractive to most palates.

The smew generally breeds in the same northern regions of the European and Asian coastlines as its larger relatives, e.g. on the salt lakes of Finland, on the northern coast of the Soviet Union in particularly large numbers, but also on some inland lakes and large rivers. The nesting season is roughly the same as the goosander's. It is a rather uncommon winter visitor to Britain.

In winter, smews associate in large flocks and fly far inland to visit lakes and waterways. The birds sometimes spend the whole winter in central Europe and may even stay until the next breeding season. Cases have been known of the northern smew being caught in central Europe, far from its northern home, as late as May, when it is almost time for it to be laying. The possibility of the birds' breeding there, near inland waters, must not be excluded. This likelihood is further supported by the fact that the smew subsists almost entirely on small fish which are plentiful in some of the waters on the Continent.

Sportsmen and bird-watchers have observed that flocks of smews frequently join up with the flocks of another northern duck, the goldeneye. Migrating flocks seen in winter were reported to be composed of both species, strongly intermingled, although they are quite different in appearance. The smew's fishy flesh is eaten only in rare localities in the north, but its eggs are consumed wholesale. The soft greyish down with which the smew lines its nests is also collected for bolster fillings.

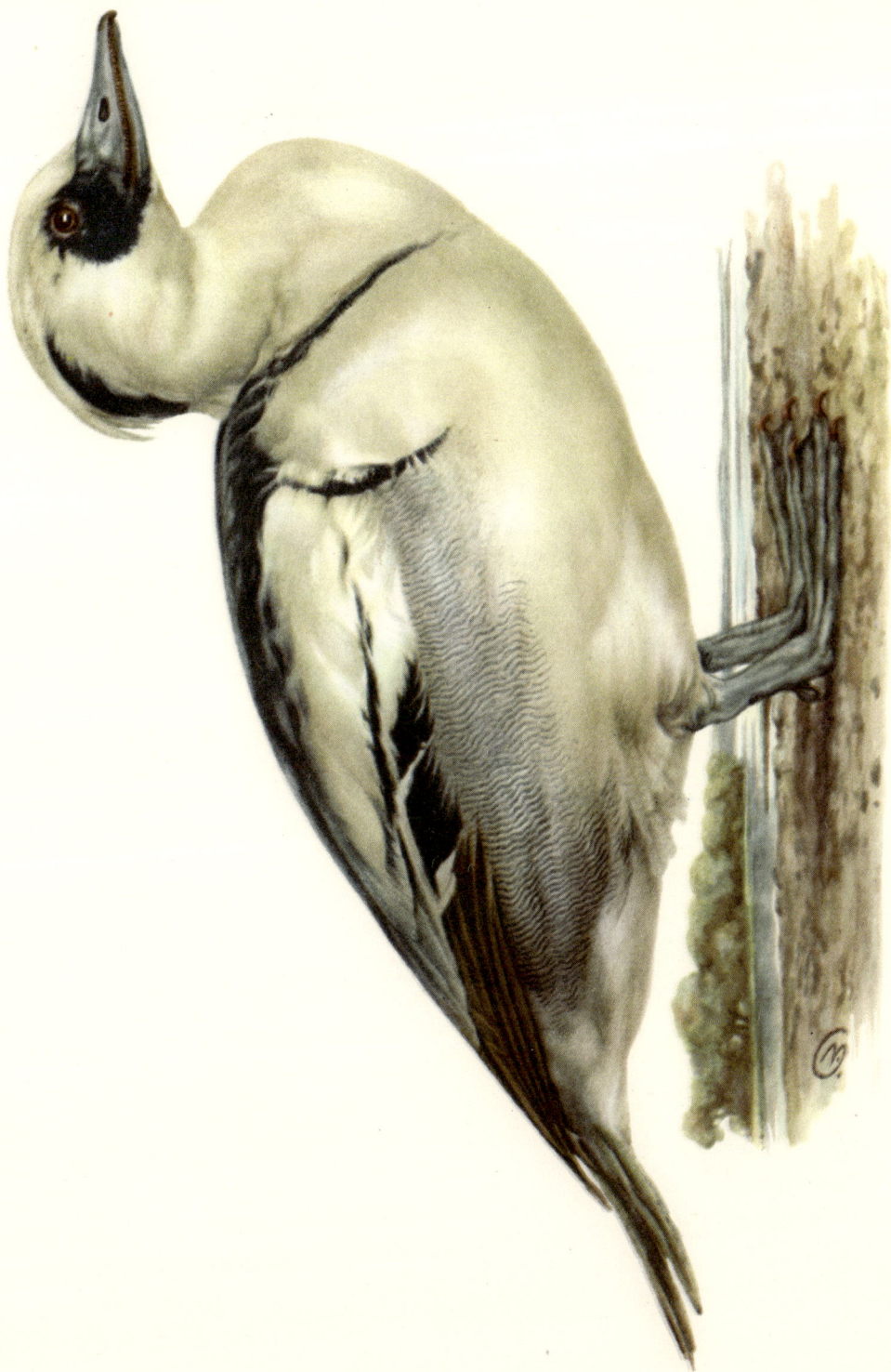

The Merganser

(MERGUS SERRATOR Linn.)

Easily distinguishable by the pretty erect and compressed crest on its head is the merganser, a bird at home in Ireland, Scotland, on many islands to the north of the Continent, and on the Baltic coast.

Somewhat smaller than the goosander, it rarely attains a wing-span of 2 ft. 9 in. (880 mm.), usually measuring only 2 ft. 7 in. (800 mm.), in the females hardly more than 1 ft. 11 in. (600 mm.). The smallest specimens correspond in size to the smew.

In the winter, medium-sized flocks of mergansers visit places where they do not nest, although in less abundant numbers than other species. They may then be met with on the North American lakes and in various places on the Continent, generally between November and May.

The Common Eider

(SOMATERIA MOLLISSIMA Linn.)

The best and lightest of eiderdowns are stuffed with the down of the common eider. The scientific name of the bird—mollissima (i.e. the softest)—serves to illustrate this fact. Now, as in ancient times, their nests are systematically pilfered by the impoverished natives on the far northern shores, to whom the sale of the down presents a stable source of income. The large eggs also serve to augment a monotonous diet. This egg collecting has been carried out so thoroughly that the birds have disappeared completely from many northern shores.

The common eider is a large bird with a heavy, ungainly body, resembling, as to size and plumpness, the well-fed domestic duck. Male adults weigh up to 5 lb. 8 oz. (2500 gm.); the eggs are of almost the same size as those of the wild goose—3 × 2 in. (780 × 520 mm.).

Nowadays, it is only in remote and rarely visited places that the birds are found in any appreciable numbers. In the more densely populated areas of the less extreme north they are either completely extinct or existing precariously, thanks to the protection of the law. The eider breeds in Greenland, Iceland, the Lofoten Islands and Spitzbergen, also on the coastline of Scotland, Ireland, Norway and Sweden, in Finland and the northern portions of the Soviet Union, as well as in the north of the American continent. Where left un-molested by humans the eider settles in colonies, the birds frequently nesting side by side. It is an extraordinarily gregarious bird, and parent birds will adopt any stray ducklings to rear alongside their own brood; stranger still, nesting mother-birds will steal each other's eggs. The nest is placed in a depression among the rocks, often at quite a distance from the water. It is lined with a thick layer of the down in such quantities that, for example, in south Greenland up to 2 metric tons (2000 kg.) of eiderdown is annually collected from one single colony. The eggs, which are dark olive in colour, are deposited in the nest as late as June.

The eider is a skilful diver and swimmer. It feeds mainly on various molluscs, supple-mented by vegetable matter. In winter eiders migrate southwards. At that time they are usually quite lean but are nevertheless shot by sportsmen. For the greater part, however, it is only the younger, not yet fully-coloured specimens that visit central European waters in winter.

The Common Scoter

(MELANITTA NIGRA Linn.)

Circumpolar sea coasts and salt lakes are the domain of an odd-looking, totally black duck with a knob on its bill, referred to by some as the raven duck. In winter, small groups of these ducks alight on inland waters, though freshwater basins are not particularly suited to their mode of life.

The flesh of the common scoter is said to be inedible, especially just after its arrival from its northern home, being still tainted by the molluscs, on which it feeds exclusively.

The common scoter is at home on the cold shores of the European and Asian north; large numbers are natives of the North American Continent, where they breed by salt-water lakes, as they do elsewhere. It breeds in the north of Scotland and Ireland, in Iceland, Spitzbergen, Norway, Sweden and Finland, in Lapland and everywhere east of Novaya Zemlya. The common scoter frequently builds its nest some distance from the water, among rocks and low brush. In June the female begins sitting on nine or ten light fawn eggs in the down-lined nest. In size, the eggs are comparable to those of our domestic hen. Adult birds are slightly smaller than mallards, their wing-span measuring from 2 ft. 4 in. to 3 ft. (720–920 mm.). Average weight is 1 lb. 12 oz. to 2 lb. 12 oz. (800–1250 gm.).

When the icy winds whistle along the northern coast, and the ocean shallows begin to freeze over, families of scoters take off on their way south to spend the winter in more congenial surroundings. We then find the birds on the coasts of Britain, France and Germany, more rarely on the Mediterranean. The common scoter visits inland waters only for rest, or if forced by strong winds. In such cases it sometimes descends half-starved on lakes and rivers of central Europe, occasionally on the Danube and other large rivers. In these places the curious black ducks—usually quite unknown to the inland sportsman—are of great interest to local naturalists.

The Velvet Scoter

(MELANITTA FUSCA Linn.)

To be met with on inland waters more frequently than the preceding species, the velvet scoter is a close relative. The drake's plumage is just as deeply black, but distinguishable from the common scoter's even at a distance by the white band below the eye and the white patch on the wings. The drake's velvety black feathers are nicely offset by the bright humped beak and the red-and-black legs. The females, however, are nondescript brownish birds, hardly differing from those of other ducks. The velvet scoter is larger than the common species, with a wing-span of 3 ft. 4 in. (1000 mm.) in the drake. When well-fed, the velvet scoter may attain a weight of 3 lb. 15 oz. (1750 gm.). The eggs, laid late in June or early July, are also larger than in the preceding species, measuring about 3×2 in. (75×46 mm.).

The velvet scoter ranges all over the forest belt of Eurasia, from the Atlantic to the Pacific. Only in exceptional places does it breed by inland lakes, notably in mountainous country. It is also at home on the western seaboard of North America.

During the winter small groups of velvet scoters visit the coasts of Britain and the southern parts of Scandinavia, as well as inland waters on the Continent. Less rare than the common scoter, the bird is well known in Germany, Czechoslovakia and Hungary. Flocks of velvet scoters will sometimes make their way south as far as the Mediterranean and have even been seen in North Africa. Inland lakes in Switzerland and Germany are regularly visited by the birds in winter. They usually stay from October till April; this varies, of course, in accordance with the weather.

Its mode of life is largely the same as the common scoter's with which it sometimes shares breeding grounds. Its fare is equally composed of tiny saltwater creatures, but it seems that the velvet scoter more easily adapts itself to freshwater fare during its long sojourn on lakes and rivers. Its flesh is hardly more pleasing to the palate; nevertheless, the birds are caught in nets *en masse* in various localities, presumably for human consumption. The soft down lining the nests is also valued highly and collected like the eider duck's.

The Mute Swan

(CYGNUS OLOR Gmelin)

Easily the best known European swan is the charming mute swan, which sometimes seems almost semi-domestic because of its attachment to humans. For this reason, swans of this species found in central Europe can hardly be regarded as truly wild birds. The swans flying over the countryside in autumn will frequently belong to some zoological gardens or public parks. Many of them, whilst remaining comparatively inactive throughout the summer, make excursions farther afield in the autumn.

The mute swan is the handsomest of all European species, with the attractive black shield over the beak which also surrounds the eye, the dignified poise of the wings and the harmonious line of its neck. Gliding over the water the mute swan is a stately spectacle, so it is not surprising that the birds have been kept on lakes and river broads from time immemorial for their decorative qualities. The Royal swans on the Thames are famous and are rigorously protected by law.

The homes of the mute swan are the lakes all over northern Europe, and portions of Asia, ranging east as far as the Pacific Ocean. Yet the mute swan breeds only in certain localities in the north, whilst some more southerly breeding grounds are the lakes of Poland, Germany, England, Turkestan, etc.

Exceeding the whooper swan in size, the mute swan may attain a weight of 31 lb. (13 620 gm.) and a wing-span of more than 8 ft. 3 in. (2500 mm.).

The Whooper Swan

(CYGNUS CYGNUS Linn.)

The 'singing swan' of northern saga and fairy-tale never refers to the better known semi-domestic mute swan but always to the yellow-beaked whooper swan. Legends and folk-tales poetically describe its trumpeting call as 'singing', and that is why in most European languages the bird's name contains a reference to song. However, though less unpleasant than the voice of other swans, to the objective observer the sound has no special charm.

The appearance of the bird is neither so proud nor so handsome as that of the mute swan, nor does it carry its head on the long thin neck in such a pleasing curve. The gait of all swans is, to say the least, ungainly, so that the birds lose much of their beauty on dry land. The whooper swan is a quarrelsome and pugnacious bird which tolerates no rival in its neighbourhood and will even attack the mute swan, chasing it from their common lake territories. There is no great difference in size between the two species, the whooper swan's weight varying from $14^{1}/_{2}$ lb. (6 750 gm.) to 28 lb. (12 700 gm.), with a wing-span of up to 8 ft. 3 in. (2 500 mm.).

The whooper swan breeds in the north of Europe and Asia, from the Atlantic to the Pacific coast, from Iceland to Greenland. Farther south fewer of the birds nest, but in rare cases they do so even as far south as the Crimea, the Caspian, in Mongolia and elsewhere. The whooper swan is a migratory bird, moving south when the northern waters freeze over, at which time it regularly visits the British coast and lakes, also Germany and the waters of central Europe. In severe winters the birds may fly south as far as southern Europe and North Africa.

The nest is placed directly on the water, often forming a floating island of broken sticks of reeds, which may be large enough to support an adult human. At the end of April, or the beginning of June, the female lays between five and seven yellowish eggs. Both parents fiercely protect the eggs, and later guard the cygnets against all potential enemies. They will usually not even allow another pair of swans on their lake, unless it is a very large one.

Bewick's Swan

(CYGNUS BEWICKII Yarr.)

Rarest of European swans, Bewick's swan is a native of the area extending from Scandinavia to the Bering Straits. It breeds in Novaya Zemlya on the island of Kolguyev and Berkhovsky, in the Lena River delta and around the coastline of the Arctic Ocean.

In winter Bewick's swan visits the shores of Britain and Ireland, in severe winters also the Continent of Europe, the Mediterranean coast and central Asia.

In appearance the bird closely resembles the whooper swan, except for its much smaller size, its weight ranging from 10 lb. 10 oz. (4900 gm.) to 15 lb. 8 oz. (6970 gm.). It carries its exceedingly long neck in a straight upright manner, not in a graceful curve, and so makes identification easy at first sight when among other swans, as in a zoo. Another distinctive mark is the yellow beak shield which does not reach the nostrils.

The Grey Lag-Goose

(ANSER ANSER Linn.)

The parent form of our white, domesticated goose is the buff-grey lag-goose which inhabits a large belt of Europe and Asia, roughly from latitude 44° to 70° north. It likes to frequent standing waters abounding in reeds and situated near meadows of fields where the birds find grazing. During migration, numerous flocks of these handsome large birds appear in almost every European country, so long as there are large sheets of water or wide rivers there. It is then that they are shot, and in countries where the grey lag-goose is a regular visitor thousands are killed every year. On the Guadalquivir estuary in Spain, where wild geese from Europe spend the winter, many thousands of birds fall victim to the local sportsmen.

In the second half of February, when the grey lag-geese return to their breeding grounds, old mates rejoin for nesting, whereas with the younger birds courtship takes place as early as the autumn. It seems probable that geese, like many other large birds, live in lifelong partnership. The nest is placed in a clump of reeds, and in April contains between four and six large buffish-white eggs. The hen sits patiently for twenty-eight days, while her mate faithfully and alertly stands guard over the nest. The newly-hatched goslings are carefully guided to the water by both parents, Mother at the head of the column and Father bringing up the rear, keeping close watch all the time. Geese have a close-knit family life, both as regards the relationship between the parents and their young, and between brothers and sisters. By the end of June the goslings are fully fledged, but they do not mate until their third year.

At the close of the summer the geese fly off to large sheets of water and go searching for food together in near-by fields and meadows. The wild geese from the north begin arriving in the milder regions of western and central Europe, while our native geese are preparing to leave in a south-westerly direction.

The Bean-Goose

(ANSER ARVENSIS Brehm)

Only a winter visitor in Britain and Central Europe is another wild goose, similar in appearance to the preceding species. It is the bean-goose, a somewhat darker bird than the grey lag-goose, with a bi- or tricoloured beak. Its size is a little smaller, but as it tends to vary greatly in all geese this rule may be hard to put to the test. Even if we accept the smaller size for this species, the span of its slender wings still exceeds—at an average of 5 ft. 11 in. (1800 mm.)—the largest corresponding measurement for the grey lag-goose of 5 ft. 7 in. (1700 mm.).

The bean-goose is a true Arctic bird, breeding in Iceland, northern Eurasia, in Spitzbergen, Greenland, and in the Soviet Union. It can generally be said to be at home in countries northwards of latitude 64° north. In these inhospitable regions the bean-goose nests in the reeds on the edges of lakes. Generally about the middle of June, it lays seven to ten eggs of slightly smaller size than those of the grey lag-goose.

In the winter the birds migrate to the south of Europe, less frequently to central and south-west Europe. The bean-goose frequents Britain and Ireland only occasionally. Wherever larger flocks of bean-geese appear in the winter months they are frequently shot and trapped.

90

The White-fronted Goose

(ANSER ALBIFRONS Scop.)

In addition to the bean-goose and the grey lag-goose, another Arctic visitor appears on our waters in autumn—the white-fronted goose, which got its scientific name from the white spot on its forehead. Its size is more or less the same as that of the other two species. The white-fronted goose also has roughly the same wing-span (4 ft. 8 in. to 5 ft. 11 in.) (1500–1800 mm.). Owing to the variations in the weight of individual birds in these species it is sometimes hard to identify the young geese, which are usually devoid of the white spot on the forehead as well as of the dark patch on the chest.

The white-fronted goose is a native of the tundras on the shores of the Arctic Ocean. It breeds in Iceland, Greenland and in some regions of the North American Continent. Its nesting habits are about the same as those of the grey lag-goose, nor do the eggs differ in size by more than a fraction of an inch.

The white-fronted goose is frequently shot in northern countries, notably before migration, when large flocks congregate in certain localities. They are also trapped in nets—for instance on the Ob river or in the Volga estuary.

The white-fronted goose spends the winter in Britain and on the Continent, visiting larger lakes and rivers in England, Germany and France. Some flocks make their way to the south of Europe or may even straggle as far as Egypt. In winter quarters the birds associate in flocks, causing them to be shot and caught in large numbers.

The Sheld-Duck

(TADORNA TADORNA Linn.)

Between the true geese and the ducks stands the colourful sheld-duck, which outrivals many an exotic bird as to beauty of plumage. It is a native of the north, breeding in separate colonies in the British Isles, northern Germany, Scandinavia, as well as France, and also on the Caspian, in Japan, northern China and Manchuria. Colonies of sheld-duck have even been seen in Spain and central Asia.

The birds usually make their nests in holes in the ground, or they may settle in some abandoned foxhole or rabbit burrow. In some parts the sheld-duck is relatively tame and unafraid and does not avoid human habitations. It does not mind settling in artificial burrows provided by the people of the north, occasionally just outside the barnyard. This practice probably originated because of the fondness of some northern islanders for the sheld-duck's large, pleasant-tasting eggs. A clutch comprises up to twelve, and large as they are they may well help to vary the diet of a fisherman's family.

The sheld-duck is a fairly large bird, attaining a weight from 2 lb. 3 oz. to 3 lb. 11 oz. (1000–1650 gm.), and a wing-span of up to 3 ft. 8 in. (1100 mm.).

The sheld-duck's winter quarters are various coastal districts in the south, not excepting North Africa, where European sheld-ducks gather on the coast and inland lakes.

The Mallard

(ANAS PLATYRHYNCHOS Linn.)

Male

The mallard is found throughout Europe, Asia and North America. During the winter months the birds migrate to regions where the waters do not freeze over and often travel as far south as North Africa.

Mallards can be easily identified during winter. The drake wears its gaily-coloured plumage only in winter and during courtship; later in the year it fades to the same drab colours as the duck. But they are at all times larger than the females and also considerably heavier. The drake weighs about 3 lb. 3 oz. (1500 gm.), the duck hardly 2 lb. 2 oz. (1000 gm.).

These birds usually feed from dusk to dawn. During the day they rest in scattered flocks on open water, swimming gently with their heads drawn back or with their bills tucked into the feathers of their backs. They will sleep on the bank and sometimes a few birds will feed sporadically at the edge of the water.

Then, in the evening, the birds go off in pairs to the ponds and ditches to seek for food. This can be animal or vegetable, their diet commonly consisting of acorns, snails, slugs, worms, insects and berries.

The mallard ranks high on the list of game-birds. Statistics in Britain show that 90 per cent are shot before they reach their third year.

In recent years a substantial decline in mallard stocks has been observed in various places in Europe, possibly because of over-intensified shooting of the birds, or it may be due to changes in habitat and food supply brought about by human agency.

The Mallard

(ANAS PLATYRHYNCHOS Linn.)

Female

The mallard makes its home, wherever possible, on European waters, sometimes settling on small expanses such as ponds in parks or even in the centre of big cities. However, it prefers waters bordered by rushes. Or again, it may nest in a hollow tree or even in artificial coops or baskets fixed low in a tree. The ducklings are capable of leaping out of such a nest from a height of up to thirty feet without coming to any harm. The mallard easily adapts itself to changed conditions and thus was readily domesticated. Several domestic strains are derived from the wild stock, all of them bred for their flesh, eggs and feathers.

The mallard ducks and drakes form into pairs in early winter, but it is not until the end of February that they visit the lakeside where they intend to build their nests. The latter are snugly lined with soft down and can frequently be found some distance from the water. Eight to fourteen oblate eggs are laid in March, olive-green or drab in colour. The mother incubates the eggs for twenty-two to twenty-six days before the lively multicoloured ducklings emerge. The hen looks after them until they are fully fledged, which is in June or July, and the family remains in the home ground till the autumn, when the young ducks take off on their own.

Mallards keep the same mate for a number of years, usually remaining together even out of the nesting season.

The Teal

(ANAS CRECCA Linn.)

A dwarf among European ducks is the teal, which scarcely attains the weight and size of the partridge. It has a wing-span of around 1 ft. 11 in. (600 mm.), weighing from $10^1/_2$ oz. to 14 oz. (300–400 gm.), exceeding this only in exceptional cases. The beak measures no more than $1^1/_4$ in. (34–38 mm.) and the legs are even shorter.

This little duck is widespread on various overgrown sheets of water in Europe, leading a mode of life much like that of its bigger cousin, the mallard. It likes to frequent boggy moors, flooded ditches and the margins of lakes, where the rushes grow thick. It keeps out of view and is inconspicuous unless disturbed, when it flies out of the rushes and over the lake. In late summer, or early autumn, the birds associate in large flocks which are joined by other flocks from the colder north. The teal is a migratory bird which arrives on its breeding grounds in the second half of March and leaves during the autumn months, though birds may be restless from late August. In winter the teal visits a number of countries where it does not normally breed. It is to be met with in Africa and south Asia, as well as all over south and western Europe. Central European teal spend the winter in Italy or France, the birds from Iceland travel to Britain for the winter, etc. After the breeding season the birds are inclined to scatter widely, and may be seen in the most diverse countries the following winter or the year after that.

Around May the teal makes its nest, laying between eight and twelve light buff or greenish eggs. The nests are often placed a fair distance from the water and may even be situated in a wood, as in the case of the mallard's nest.

During duck shoots fair numbers of teal may be taken, particularly in localities where the birds congregate prior to migration. It is a good table bird, but its small size and fairly sporadic incidence give it a secondary importance from the point of view of shooting.

The Garganey

(ANAS QUERQUEDULA Linn.)

Somewhat larger than the teal is the equally colourful garganey. These ducks are even more plentiful in the lake districts of central and western Europe than their cousins. The garganey has a wing-span of about 2 ft. to 2 ft. 2¹/₂ in. (607–664 mm.) and may reach a weight of more than 14 oz. (400 gm.). The birds are rather heavier in autumn, as they put on a fair amount of fat to be able to withstand the rigours of a migration.

The garganey frequently builds its nest right in the water, on piles of rushes or shelves of sedge. The eggs of this species are slightly larger than those of the teal—their colour is creamy white with a buff tinge.

The garganey is widely distributed as a breeding bird in the northern parts of Europe and Asia. It is mainly a summer visitor to Britain. The birds spend the winter on any open expanse of water all over the Continent, except in the north. Garganeys ringed in Finland have been shot on Lake Geneva, others ringed in Czechoslovakia were taken in Italy. Some northern garganeys winter in England and Ireland.

The Wigeon
(ANAS PENELOPE Linn.)

In autumn, larger sheets of water are visited by the handsome wigeon, a close relative of the mallard. The male utters a distinctive call, pleasant to the ear and rather like a whistle.

The wigeon breeds to the north of Europe. In autumn, on their way south, the birds frequent all of western and central Europe. The wigeon's own home ground is the belt ranging from Iceland and the British Isles in the west, to the Soviet Union and northern Manchuria in the east. The ringing of wigeons has shown that the young birds fly in every direction in their first winter, so that birds ringed in Iceland arrived in England, France, Spain and Italy, as well as in the southern portions of the Soviet Union. Wigeons frequently breed at a great distance from their birthplace in the following spring, and specimens ringed in Britain were found nesting on the middle Volga the year after. There are records of Icelandic wigeons crossing the Atlantic to North America where the similar American wigeon breeds. It usually frequents inland waters, keeping away from the coast.

In autumn flocks of wigeons are on the move as early as the middle of September, when they visit the well-watered regions of southern Europe. The flocks generally make their way back north in April, but occasionally stay on in central Europe till summer.

The wigeon makes its nest near the margin of lakes and ponds, or at a distance from the water. Being a good walker, it is less dependent on the water than other ducks. In May a clutch of between eight and ten light buff eggs is in the nest, measuring about $2^1/_2$ in. $\times$ $1^1/_2$ in. (53×39 mm.). After hatching, the female takes her brood to the water and looks after the family, unassisted by the drake. Wigeons like to graze in lakeside meadows, vegetable food playing a far greater part in their diet than in that of other ducks.

The Pintail

(ANAS ACUTA Linn.)

The elongated tail feathers give the northern pintail its distinctive name. It is a strikingly slender duck, only slightly smaller than the mallard, as regards wing-span and weight. The weight varies from 1 lb. 3 oz. to 2 lb. 12 oz. (540–1250 gm.) in both sexes, and the wing-span may be over 3 ft. (960 mm.).

Breeding throughout northern Europe, Asia and North America, the pintail sometimes nests farther south, even in central Europe. Distribution of the species in Europe is from latitude 45° north, from Iceland to the Arctic coast and along the Volga River, in Asia down to the southern portion of Ussuri. The pintail migrates to the south of Europe and spends the winter around the Mediterranean, while the Asian variety goes to the south of Asia. European pintails are sometimes seen in North Africa, even on the Upper Nile and in Senegal.

The birds usually visit central Europe only during migration, in March on their way north, from October onwards in their southward journey. They pass over river beds and lakes, taking rests in order to conserve their strength for the long trip. Ringing of the birds has established that pintails—similarly to wigeons—disperse in various directions after the breeding season. Birds ringed on the Volga were seen in Bulgaria and in Egypt in the winter, also in the south of France. Icelandic pintails have visited England and Italy in winter and Sweden in autumn.

The pintail makes its nest in a dry place, sometimes quite a long way from the water, in the shelter of a bush or in tufts of high grass. Late in April, or in the first half of May, we find a clutch of between six and ten greenish-grey or greenish-buff eggs in the nest. The lively baby ducks hatch out in twenty-eight days and are taken care of by their mother alone.

The Gadwall

(ANAS STREPERA Linn.)

Resembling the mallard more closely than any other species of duck, the gadwall is somewhat smaller in size. There is less divergence between the sexes than in other species, both birds resembling the mallard drake except for the white patches on the gadwall's wings. The wing-span is about 2 ft. 8 in. to 2 ft. 10 in. (802–865 mm.), and the weight is considerably less than the mallard's.

The gadwall is distributed over a large portion of the northern hemisphere, from Iceland and Britain to Italy, the Balkan peninsula and the Soviet Union. It is also at home all over northern Asia to the easternmost tip, as well as in North America. The gadwall spends the winter in the south of Europe or in Africa.

Flocks of gadwalls take off on their way to the south early in September, arriving in large numbers at places where they are unknown during the summer, or where only a few pairs nest. The gadwall returns to its breeding grounds after the middle of March. The birds make their way in pairs to various inland waters while the main group continues on its way north. As gadwalls like to hide during the nesting season, opinions differ greatly on their abundance. Whereas some authorities consider the gadwall to be a widespread bird, others describe it as a rare species.

The gadwall builds its nest on dry ground among the reeds, occasionally at a fair distance from the water, and cases are known of gadwalls' nests in inland fields or meadows. The bird lines its nest with dark down, and in this cosy feather-bed it deposits from eight to twelve cream-coloured or ochre-yellowish eggs late in May or early in June. The eggs measure $2^1/_4$ in. $\times 1^1/_2$ in. (55 $\times$ 40 mm.)—i.e. roughly the same as the mallard's. The newly-hatched ducklings, too, look almost like young mallards.

The Shoveller

(SPATULA CLYPEATA Linn.)

Identifying the shoveller is an easy matter because of the large size and width of its curious beak, which may measure up to $2^3/_4$ in. in length and $1^1/_2$ in. across the tip (70 mm., 37 mm.). It is indeed a very unusual adornment for the narrow head of a duck. The inside of the shoveller's beak is lined with a strongly developed network of horny plates and teeth which enable the duck to find its food. Unlike the other species related to it, the shoveller feeds on animal matter, which it shovels up from the muddy beds of shallow waters. For this reason this otherwise abundant duck is absent from some lakes and rivers, as it keeps out of the way of basins where small creatures and plankton are not to be found in sufficient amounts. This is also why the shoveller is difficult to keep in captivity and therefore only rarely seen in zoos.

In Europe, the shoveller breeds near suitable ponds and cannot be described as a rare bird, although neither is it widespread. But it is a regular visitor to inland waterways on its way south in autumn, and again when it returns in spring. The shoveller starts its winter flight as early as August, to return to its breeding grounds in March. Those which choose continental lakes for nesting begin doing so at the end of April, concentrating on sheltered spots among the rushes. In May, or later, we find the nest containing between seven and twelve russet-tinged white eggs, of somewhat smaller size than the mallard's.

The ducks themselves are also smaller than the mallard, having a wing-span of 2 ft. 4 in. to 2 ft. $7^1/_2$ in. (720–800 mm.). Their weight ranges from 1 lb. to 2 lb. (450–900 gm.) —i.e. roughly the same as smaller specimens of female mallards. The female shoveller also resembles these in its plumage, so that we may confuse the two species unless we notice the large beak.

Shovellers are distributed over the territory from the Atlantic to the Pacific, from Alaska in the north to California in the south. In the winter the shoveller is frequent in the south of Europe, North Africa, India and south China.

The Red-crested Pochard

(NETTA RUFINA Pallas)

Besides the true ducks, which can fairly easily be classified as one genus—and which are sometimes referred to as surface-feeding ducks—numerous representatives of yet another group make their home on European waters: the diving ducks, deriving their name from the way they forage for food. The members of the latter group are distinguished by their ability to dive far below the surface, in the manner of grebes.

Easily the handsomest among the diving ducks is the red-crested pochard, deriving its name from the large crest worn by both sexes, which is bright orange in the drake so that it looks like pure gold in the sunshine. The red beak also contributes towards making the species truly ornamental ducks.

The red-crested pochard is a fairly large duck, almost equalling the mallard in size; seen outdoors it seems even larger than the latter. Its wing-span is roughly 3 ft. 3 in. (980 mm.)—i.e. only slightly less than in the mallard drake; also its weight is about the same, 1 lb. 10 oz. to 2 lb. 15 oz. (800–1360 gm.).

The habitats of this beautiful duck are large sheets of standing water, from the Mediterranean to Mongolia, but during migration it visits various European and Asian countries. In some localities, such as Britain, the red-crested pochard is extremely rare, and survives only thanks to the strictest protection. Where red-crested pochards are protected in bird reserves the number of breeding birds has increased during recent years.

In spring, about mid-March, families and flocks of red-crested pochards begin returning to their breeding grounds, while their southward flight sometimes occurs as early as late July. The nest of these ducks is a pile, up to 1 ft. 8 in. (500 mm.) in height, usually placed immediately on the water, less frequently on islets of reeds. The eggs are light greyish-buff or dirty off-white in colour.

The Common Pochard

(AYTHYA FERINA Linn.)

The common pochard can be distinguished from all other ducks even at a distance, by the peculiar colouring of the drakes, even more distinctive in the sunlight, which accentuates their silvery sheen against the water, with the heads a bright red.

When swimming the birds settle down deep in the water, so that only the white, black-banded flanks and the red heads show above the surface. The weight of the common pochard almost equals that of the female mallard—generally from 1 lb. 8 oz. to 2 lb. 13 oz. (680–1300 gm.), but it is smaller in size, its wing-span being only 2 ft. 8 in. (780 mm.). The common pochard is a very chubby little duck, particularly in autumn when the body puts on reserves of fat for the winter. It feeds on vegetable matter as well as on the small creatures on the water's bed. An excellent diver, the common pochard is capable of remaining under the water for up to half a minute. It can dive to a depth of 8 ft.

The bird is at home throughout Europe and the greater part of Asia, migrating in the winter to North Africa and China, among other places. Some flocks of pochards apparently breed fairly far to the south, even in North Africa, while their northern nesting grounds include the British Isles, as well as Lake Ladoga and other localities in the northern part of the Soviet Union. Some stay on over the winter in Britain and their flocks can be observed on the open water in the middle of frozen lakes.

The duck has a dark brown head and neck with greyish white cheeks and chin. The breast and upper parts are reddish brown, the latter shading into greyish brown, crossed by wavy grey lines.

The pochards arrive at their nesting grounds in March, and in mid-May we find their nests with the lining of soft blackish down from the autumn moult on tussocks of sedge and in the reeds. The nests are bulky structures of rushes and flags, raised well above the ground, never far from and often actually over water.

The clutch comprises between six and twelve large greenish or bluish eggs. The nestling is olive-grey above and buff beneath, and has a buff eye-stripe and small buff patches on the wing.

After nesting, the ducks make their home in waters thickly overgrown with water plants, where tiny creatures abound. When stopping for brief rests on their autumn flight they also prefer such waters, particularly large expanses. Occasionally they will visit big rivers as well.

Some claim that pochard flesh is good to eat, but it is generally regarded as inferior to that of other ducks. In some parts of Europe pochards gathering for migration are caught *en masse* in nets stretched across their path; in other places, again, they are standard shooting birds.

The Ferruginous Duck

(AYTHYA NYROCA Güld.)

The ferruginous duck is a miniature edition of the common pochard, yet in mode of life and character it differs greatly from its larger cousin. Whereas the common pochard is gregarious and likes to associate in large flocks, being quite content to have neighbours during nesting, the ferruginous duck is the individualist of the duck world. It never appears in flocks on the lake—it is generally met with only as a few pairs among the other aquatic birds—and in the mating season the drake fiercely fights all rivals, as well as some that he only thinks may qualify as such. At that time the drakes seem to be all over the place, their screaming can be heard from a distance, and sportsmen claim that they are so busy fighting one another that they quite forget their customary wariness.

Though very much like its bigger cousin as to colouring and shape, the ferruginous duck can be identified from afar by the distinctive white patches on the wings, and the paler red head. Adult birds are also conspicuous for having white irides, whereas the ducklings' irides are brown. The ferruginous duck is only slightly larger than the teal, with a wing-span not exceeding 2 ft. 4 in. (690 mm.). Weight varies widely according to sex, age and season, between 14 oz. and 1 lb. 8 oz. (400–700 gm.). The beak measures scarcely $1^1/_3$ in. (40 mm.), as against 2 in. (49 mm.) in the common pochard.

The ferruginous duck makes its home in the milder portions of Europe and Asia, from central Europe to the Mediterranean. Large numbers breed along the Volga, Don and Dniester rivers, and all over Asia as far as Tibet and Tyan-Shan. The ferruginous duck occasionally appears in Britain and migrates to North Africa, as far south as Egypt. The autumn flight begins in October, and the spring return to the nesting grounds usually takes place in the middle of March.

Nests are generally placed on smallish muddy ponds, with plenty of rushes and reeds around the banks, or they may be situated some distance away from the water. In May, or early June, between six and fourteen reddish-yellow eggs with a greenish tinge are deposited in the nest.

The Tufted Duck

(AYTHYA FULIGULA Linn.)

A small member of this group is the tufted duck—so called from the overhanging crest which is particularly distinctive in the drake. We can recognise it on the water, even from a distance, by its black feathers and the snowy white patches on its flanks. Its mode of life differs somewhat from that of even its closest relatives. Subsisting on molluscs and crustaceans, it has to dive constantly in its quest for food. The tufted duck is an accomplished diver, capable of staying under water for a full 50 seconds. Experts claim that it can dive to a depth of 11 ft. When flushed, the tufted duck's first instinct is to save itself by diving, taking wing only when the danger is extreme.

The tufted duck is not much smaller in size than the common pochard, its wing-span being 2 ft. $4^1/_2$ in.–2 ft. $5^1/_2$ in. (720–740 mm.), and its weight about 1 lb. 2 oz. to 2 lb. 2 oz. (500 to 1000 gm.).

It is native to parts of Europe and Asia, from latitude 70° north down to more southerly parts, and from the Atlantic to the Pacific. In Britain and central Europe the tufted duck is a winter visitor, a passage migrant, and often also a breeding resident. Small groups of tufted ducks may be seen in places where they are normally unknown, even on large rivers in the city, in winter time. Their migration lasts from October to April.

The tufted duck likes to make its nest by the margin of larger overgrown ponds and lakes, usually about May or June. It is a gregarious bird, often placing its nests side by side. It lays between six and ten greyish-brown eggs, which are somewhat smaller than the common pochard's, yet larger than those of the ferruginous duck.

The tufted duck is not normally shot, as its flesh, like that of all water-fowl feeding predominantly on small creatures, is rather unpleasant to the taste.

The Scaup Duck

(AYTHYA MARILA Linn.)

Frequently in autumn, but sometimes also in spring, flocks of curious-looking ducks arrive on British and central European waters, which are of roughly the same size as the common pochard and the tufted duck, and which they also resemble in colouring. In fact, they do look rather like a cross-breed of the two. Their heads and breasts are black like the tufted duck's, whereas their backs are light-coloured like the common pochard's. As a rule they do not stay in the same spot for long, so that bird-watchers can never be quite sure.

These are scaup ducks, which are at home high up on the Arctic coast, in Iceland, on the Finnish lakes, in northern Asia and on the North American Continent. There are rare cases of the scaup duck breeding in Scotland. Its regular haunts are in the belt between the 50th and 70th Parallels, where the birds abound in some areas, for example in Iceland.

They usually make their home in shallow bays, finding their animal food by deftly diving for it to a depth of up to 10 ft. The scaup duck's staple diet are molluscs and crustaceans, and according to some who have tried its flesh is inedible at that time. Nevertheless, on some northern shores the birds have traditionally been trapped in large nets stretched across their path—probably for lack of other game.

Late in September, or in October, when the northern home of the scaup duck becomes ever more inhospitable with the arrival of snowstorms and drift-ice, the birds take off on their flight south. At that time they visit various inland waters, at least for a short rest. They fly on to the south, to Cyprus, Egypt or Arabia. Asian scaup ducks go to China and Japan for the winter. Ringing has established that a scaup duck bred in Iceland spent the winter in France, one from Finland on the Dalmatian coast. In February or March the scaup duck returns to its northern homeland, remaining in our latitudes for the summer only in rare instances.

The Goldeneye

(BUCEPHALA CLANGULA Linn.)

A regular winter visitor to Britain and central Europe is the goldeneye, easily distinguished from all other ducks by its large, apparently compressed head and the striking white patch on the face of the male. In size it is comparable to the common pochard, with an average wing-span of 2 ft. 6 in. (750 mm.), and a weight of 1 lb. 5 oz. to 2 lb. 7 oz. (600–1130 gm.).

The goldeneye is a native of Finland, Iceland, Scandinavia, the northern portions of the Soviet Union, also of eastern Asia and the North American Continent. It now only very rarely nests in Britain. In the autumn, usually about October or November, flocks of goldeneye arrive on inland waters, to take off again—a few days or a week later—for the south. They generally spend the winter in the south of Europe, but some remain over the winter. Flocks of goldeneyes have been known to descend on large rivers, even in the centre of cities. The goldeneye associates in large flocks, often comprising two or three hundred birds. Flocks composed entirely of the drakes have been observed in central Europe while the females and younger birds spent the winter farther to the south.

The goldeneye will frequently make its nest in a hollow tree, a fact put to good use by some northern people who make the laying duck a substitute for the domestic hen. On the banks of waters where goldeneye breed in large numbers they hang large nesting boxes with big openings in the trees, and when the female goldeneye has made its home in one of these and lays its first clutch of between eight and fourteen bluish-green large eggs (measurements $2^1/_2 \times 1^3/_4$ in. to 60×42 mm.), they are collected one after the other. In this way the goldeneye is forced to lay up to three times its normal number of eggs. The goldeneye is an excellent diver, its food consisting entirely of animal matter. That is why it is not regarded as a good table bird.

The Buffel-headed Duck

(BUCEPHALA ALBEOLA Linn.)

A rare visitor to the west of Europe is the North American buffel-headed duck, which is much smaller than its cousin, the goldeneye. The wing of the drake measures scarcely 7 in. (180 mm.), as compared with $9^1/_4$ in. (240 mm.) for the goldeneye drake.

The breeding grounds of this handsome duck are the lakes in the north of the American Continent; it occasionally crosses the Atlantic to Europe, and several specimens have been shot in the British Isles.

The buffel-headed duck nests in hollow trees, in the same manner as its European relative. Nor are its other habits and general mode of life markedly different.

The Long-tailed Duck

(CLANGULA HYEMALIS Linn.)

Yet another member of the group of diving ducks often makes its way to west and central Europe in the late autumn—the long-tailed duck. Its range extends over the northern portions of Europe, Asia and North America, and its domain is almost exclusively the coastal strips. It feeds on all kinds of tiny creatures, notably molluscs, worms and small crustacea. At that time its flesh has quite an unpleasant taste, with a fishy flavour. This gradually disappears after the birds have spent some time on inland waters, having to make do with the same fare as other ducks. It is a skilful diver, capable of submerging to considerable depths. Like all other inhabitants of the far inhospitable north, the long-tailed duck is very tame and will allow humans to approach within a few feet. It breeds among the rocks on the seashore, in tussocks of grass, around the middle of June. Its eggs are from six to ten in number, and light grey in colour.

In autumn the birds leave their native shores and northern lakes to migrate south and make their winter home on the inland waters of more populated areas. They visit England, France, Belgium, Hungary, Northern Italy and other European countries. In their winter quarters they form small groups and keep to lakes and larger rivers.

We can identify the long-tailed duck by the odd shape of its short beak, upright forehead, and—as its name suggests—by the elongated tail feathers of the drake. The white head of the adult male attracts attention even at a distance. The long-tailed duck has a wing-span of about 2 ft. 4 in. (700 mm.) and an approximate weight of 1 lb. 2 oz. (550 gm.).

The Harlequin Duck

(HISTRIONICUS HISTRIONICUS Linn.)

A casual winter visitor to European coastal waters, but very rarely to Britain, is a small gaily-coloured duck which readily attracts attention by its unusual appearance and peculiar way of moving along the water. In its agility and continual diving activity, it is reminiscent of the grebe or the coot. Its multicoloured plumage is striking among our more soberly clad birds. This winter guest from Iceland, Greenland, Siberia, or even from North America, is the harlequin duck. Authorities classify this curious little duck as belonging to the genus closely related to that of the goldeneye.

A smallish bird, approaching in size to that of the common pochard, the average wing-span is 2 ft. 8 in. (800 mm.) and the weight from 1 lb. 2 oz. to 1 lb. 13 oz. (500–800 gm.).

Native haunts of the harlequin duck are the rocky coasts of the extreme north. The birds generally breed far from the shore by freshwater lakes among clumps of grass and bushes. The pale tan eggs are from four to eight in number.

When the short northern summer draws to a close, groups of harlequin ducks rise and make off for more southerly and south-westerly parts. They are then met on the Caspian and the Sea of Aral, in the north of Germany, on the Elbe, Rhine and Main rivers and the Upper Danube, as far south as Lake Constance.

The harlequin duck is also a native of the North American continent, where it can be found at all the northern lakes during the summer months. There it abounds in numbers even greater than on the Siberian steppes.

The Wood-Pigeon

(COLUMBA PALUMBUS Linn.)

Largest of European wild pigeons, the wood-pigeon frequents the larger woods, not too far from cornfields. While it will peck the seeds of all kinds of weeds on the edge of the wood, its favourite nourishment is found in the fields, particularly after harvesting. That is the time when the birds are most conspicuous, as it is then that they associate in flocks. In September or October the flocks unite with others in great hosts, migrating from central Europe in a southerly or south-westerly direction towards Spain, Portugal, Italy, occasionally also to West Africa.

The return trip generally takes place about the middle of March, and one month later the flat nest contains two white eggs. The nest is so flimsy that the eggs may be seen through the loosely woven structure. Both parents take turns in incubating the eggs for seventeen to nineteen days; again, both share the task of feeding their brood. Wood-pigeons sometimes breed twice or even three times during a summer. During courtship, the males call and fly about above the trees with much flapping of wings, in the same way as some species of domestic pigeons.

The wood-pigeon is a fairly large bird, with a wing-span of 2 ft. 7 in. (780 mm.) and weighing more than 1 lb. (500 gm.). A game-bird, it is a challenge to the sportsman through its exceeding caution, so that bagging the wood-pigeon is no mean feat. Where wood-pigeons are left unmolested they become almost tame, as for example in the parks and avenues of London and Paris.

The wood-pigeon's habitat extends over almost all of Europe and Asia as far south as the Himalayas and West Africa. It ranges northwards as far as latitude 62° north, notably in Scandinavia.

The Stock-Dove

(COLUMBA OENAS Linn.)

In deciduous forests and in places with plenty of hollow trees lives a small wild pigeon, the stock-dove, which corresponds in size to the medium-sized domestic strains. Its wing-span is about 2 ft. 1 in. (630 mm.), its average weight $10^1/_2$ oz. (300 gm.).

The stock-dove returns to its nesting grounds in the first half of March, though earlier returns have been recorded. Some of the birds may remain the whole winter. Shortly after arrival the birds go about finding suitable hollows in old trees, or they may settle in abandoned hollows. If sufficient hollows are not available they willingly make their home in artificial nesting boxes, provided that the opening is at least $3^3/_4$ in. (90 mm.) wide, and the box perfectly rain-proof. In places, the provision of nesting-boxes has resulted in a remarkable increase of the stock-dove population. Especially at the present time, when every hollow tree has to be removed to check the spread of infection and parasites, nesting boxes ought to be hung up to relieve the stock-dove's housing shortage.

In the first half of April two eggs appear in the nest, and are hatched after seventeen or eighteen days' incubation by both parents. A second clutch is usually laid in June, while cases of a third are not unknown. For the second lay, however, the stock-dove finds a new hollow.

Late in the summer, the birds associate in flocks which are frequently quite numerous. Mixed flocks of stock-dove and wood-pigeon have also been observed. From central Europe the birds may fly to Spain, or to Albania, but the greater part of British stock-doves stay at home throughout the winter.

The stock-dove is to be found all over Europe, ranging southwards from latitude 65° north. It is also at home in Asia Minor, Iran, and in north and north-west Africa.

INDEX